THE GROWN-UPS' BOOK OF BOOKS

D0366089

The Grown-Ups' Book of Books

In celebration of

1999

Published in association with
Headline Book Publishing Ltd

This compilation copyright © Headline Book Publishing Ltd 1999

The acknowledgements on pages 172-177 constitute
an extension of this copyright page

The moral right of the authors has been asserted in accordance
with the Copyright, Designs and Patents Act 1988.

THE GROWN-UPS' BOOK OF BOOKS has been compiled
and produced by Headline Book Publishing Ltd

First published in 1999

10 9 8 7 6 5 4 3 2 1

All rights reserved. No part of this publication may be
reproduced, stored in a retrieval system, or transmitted
in any form or by any means without the prior written
permission of the publisher, nor be otherwise circulated
in any form of binding or cover other than that in which
it is published and without a similar condition being
imposed on the subsequent purchaser.

ISBN 0 7472 6089 3

Typeset free of charge for World Book Day by
Letterpart Limited, Reigate, Surrey

Printed free of charge for World Book Day
in Great Britain by
Caledonian International Book Manufacturing Ltd, Glasgow

HEADLINE BOOK PUBLISHING
A division of Hodder Headline PLC
338 Euston Road
London NW1 3BH

Sponsors and Supporters of World Book Day

World Book Day 1999 is an initiative sponsored by booksellers and publishers and supported by the printing industry. It is run in association with the BBC.

A number of organizations have contributed to World Book Day 1999, through financial sponsorship or support in kind, including: The Booksellers Association of Great Britain and Ireland; the Publishers Association; Clé/Irish Book Publishers Association; the Basic Skills Agency; Book Tokens Ltd; News International; the Department for Education and Employment; the Department of Trade and Industry; and Yale University Press.

The organizers would also like to thank:

Publishers

Major contributors: HarperCollins*Publishers*; Hodder Headline plc; Little, Brown & Company; Macmillan Publishers Ltd; Penguin Books Ltd; Random House UK Ltd; Transworld Publishers Ltd.

Other contributors: A & C Black (Publishers) Ltd; BBC Worldwide; Bloomsbury Publishing plc; Constable & Company; André Deutsch Ltd; Egmont Children's Books; Faber & Faber; Oxford University Press; Scholastic Ltd; Simon & Schuster; Usborne Publishing; Walker Books Ltd; The Watts Group

Booksellers

Most booksellers in the UK and Ireland are supporting World Book Day through the cost of redeeming free book vouchers. The organizers would like to thank the following in particular:

Bertrams the Book Wholesaler; Bookland; Books *etc*; Borders; Dillons the Bookstore; Gardners Books Ltd; Hammicks Bookshops Ltd; James Thin; Lomond Books; Mahers the Booksellers; Methuens; Wesley Owen; WH Smith plc; Sussex Stationers; THE Books; Waterstone's Booksellers Ltd.

Designers

Head Design

Printers and Manufacturers

Borregaard Hellefos A/S; Caledonian International Book Manufacturing Ltd; Clays Ltd; William Clowes Ltd; Concise Cover Printers Ltd; Creative Print & Design Group; Enso Publication Papers Ltd; Farringdon Printers Ltd; Iggesund Board Suppliers; Letterpart Ltd; Mackays of Chatham plc; Martins the Printers Ltd; Metsa Serla; Norske Skog Ltd; Saxon Photolitho Ltd; Shalefield; White Quill Press.

Distribution

HarperCollins*Publishers*; Eason & Son Ltd; Bertrams the Book Wholesaler; Gardners Books Ltd; STL; THE Books.

The organizers would also like to thank all those supporters who have contributed to the campaign since *The Children's Book of Books 1999* and *The Grown-Ups' Book of Books* went to press.

Contents

Foreword

Despite reports to the contrary, adults are people too. Last World Book Day millions of parents, me included, drooled enviously as their children, hands, for once, miraculously unclenched from the remote control, pored over the delightful – utterly free – *Children's Book of Books*. This year, I'm thrilled to say, it's our turn as well. Welcome to the enchanting *Grown-Ups' Book of Books*, crammed full of the most gripping and glorious modern writing. Laughter, tears and a sure-fire recipe for happiness – not bad for only £1 or a World Book Day voucher.

There's something here to titillate every taste bud: a haunting poem from the late Ted Hughes, a Discworld offering from fantastic fantasist Terry Pratchett, the chance to tiptoe through the tulips with Deborah Moggach and a juicy morsel of Louis de Bernières. They join a battalion of bestselling authors including Nicholas Evans, Sarah Dunant and Jeffrey Archer.

World Book Day, held on April 23rd, Shakespeare's birthday, is the biggest annual celebration of books and reading. To make this a truly worldwide event, there will be fund-raising events nationwide to raise money for Book Aid International – the charity that donates books to schools in developing countries. Who knows? *The*

Grown-Ups' Book of Books might just inspire you to leap out of your comfy reading chair and take part.

Have an irresistible time enjoying your favourite authors and discovering a whole host of future favourites. Shakespeare would be proud.

Vanessa Feltz xx

Something for Nothing

by Jeffrey Archer

Jeffrey Archer is the author of ten outstanding novels and three collections of short stories, all of which have been huge international bestsellers. His most recent novel, The Eleventh Commandment, *has even caused the CIA to review their procedures.*

Jake began to dial the number slowly as he had done every evening at six o'clock ever since his father had passed away. For the next fifteen minutes he settled back to listen to what his mother had done that day.

She led such a sober, orderly life that she rarely had anything of interest to tell him, least of all on a Saturday. She had coffee every morning with her oldest friend, Mollie Preston, and some days that would last until lunch. On Mondays, Wednesdays and Fridays she played bridge with the Taylors across the road; on Tuesdays and Thursdays she visited her sister, Nancy, but at least that gave her something to grumble about when he rang on those particular evenings.

On Saturdays she rested from the rigours of the week. Her only strenuous activity was to purchase the bulky Sunday edition of the *Times* just after lunch, a strange New York tradition, which at least gave her the chance to tell her son what stories he should look at from its three hundred pages the following day.

1

For Jake, each evening's conversation would consist of a few appropriate questions, depending on the day. Monday, Wednesday, Friday: How did the bridge go? How much did you win/lose? Tuesday, Thursday: How is Aunt Nancy? Really? That bad? Saturday: Anything interesting in the *Times* that I should be looking at tomorrow?

Observant readers will be aware that there are seven days in any given week and will now be wanting to know about Sunday. On Sunday, Jake's mother always came to lunch with the family, so there was no need to call her that evening.

Jake dialled the last digit of his mother's number, and waited for her to pick up the phone. He prepared himself to be told what would be in tomorrow's *New York Times*. It usually took two or three rings before she answered the phone, the amount of time required for her to walk from her chair by the fire to the phone on the other side of the room. When the tone continued past four, five, six, even seven rings, Jake began to wonder if she might be out. But that wasn't possible. She was never out at six o'clock, winter or summer. She kept to a routine so regular that it would have brought a smile to the lips of a marine sergeant.

Finally he heard a click. He had just begun to say 'Hi, Mom, it's Jake' when he heard a voice that was certainly not his mother's, and that was already in mid-conversation. Realizing he'd got a crossed line, he was about to put the phone down when he heard the voice say, 'There'll be a hundred thousand dollars in it for you. All you have to do is turn up and collect it. It's in an envelope for you at Billy's.'

'So where's Billy's?' said a new voice.

'On the corner of Oak Street and Randall. They'll be expecting you around eight.'

Jake tried not to breathe in or out as he wrote 'Oak and Randall' on the pad by the phone.

'How will they know the envelope is for me?' asked the second voice.

'You just ask for a copy of the *New York Times* and hand over a hundred-dollar bill. He'll give you a quarter change, as if you'd handed him a dollar. That way, if there's anyone else in the shop, they won't be suspicious. Don't open the envelope until you're in a safe place: there are a lot of people who'd like to get their hands on a hundred thousand dollars. And whatever you do, don't ever contact me again. If you do, it won't be a pay-off you'll get next time.'

The line went dead.

Jake hung up, having completely forgotten that he was supposed to be ringing his mother.

He sat down and considered what to do next . . . if anything. Ellen had taken the kids to a movie, as she did every Saturday, and they weren't expected back until nine. His dinner was in the microwave, with a note to tell him how many minutes it would take to cook. He always added one minute.

Jake found himself flicking through the A-F telephone directory. He turned over the pages until he reached B: Bi . . . Bil . . . Billy . . . Billy's. And there it was, at 1127 Oak Street. He closed the directory and walked through to his den, where he searched through the bookshelf behind his desk for his gazette of New York. He found it wedged in between Elisabeth Schwarzkopf's memoirs and *How to Lose Twenty Pounds When You're Over Forty*.

He turned to the index in the back and quickly found the right page. He checked the grid reference and placed his finger on the correct square. He calculated that it would take him thirty or forty minutes to get over the West Side. He checked his watch. It was 6.14. What was he thinking? He had no intention of going anywhere. To start with, he didn't have a hundred dollars.

Jake took out his wallet from the inside pocket of his jacket. Thirty-seven dollars. He walked through to the kitchen to check Ellen's petty-cash box. It was locked, and he couldn't remember where she hid the key. He took a screwdriver from the drawer below the hob and forced the box open. Another twenty-two dollars. He paced around the kitchen, trying to think. And then he remembered.

He left the kitchen and went up to his daughter's room. Suzie's Snoopy moneybox was on her dressing table. He picked it up and walked over to the bed, where he turned the box upside down, shaking all the coins out on to the quilt. Seven dollars and seventy-five cents.

He sat on the end of the bed, desperately trying to concentrate, then recalled the fifty-dollar bill he always kept folded in his driving licence for emergencies. He did a quick mental calculation: one hundred and sixteen dollars and seventy-five cents.

Jake checked his watch. It was 6.23. He would just go and take a look. No more, he told himself.

He took his old overcoat from the hall cupboard and left the apartment, checking as he did so that all three locks on the front door were securely bolted. He pressed the elevator button, but there was no sound. Out of order again, Jake thought, and began jogging down the stairs. Across the street was a bar he often had a drink at when Ellen took the children to the movies.

The barman smiled when he came in. 'The usual?' he asked, somewhat surprised to see Jake wearing a heavy overcoat to cross the road.

'No thanks,' said Jake, trying to sound casual. 'I just wondered if you had a hundred-dollar bill.'

'Not sure if I do,' the barman replied. He rummaged around in a stack of notes, then turned back to Jake. 'You're lucky. Just the one.'

Jake handed over the fifty, a twenty, two tens and five ones, and received in exchange a one-hundred-dollar bill. Folding the note carefully in four, he slipped it into his wallet, which he returned to the inside pocket of his jacket, then left the bar and walked out on to the street.

He ambled slowly for two blocks, until he came to a bus stop. Perhaps he would get there too late, and the problem would take care of itself, he thought. A bus drew into the kerb. Jake climbed the steps, paid his fare and took a seat near the back, still uncertain what he planned to do when he reached the West Side.

He was so deep in thought that he missed his stop and had to walk almost a mile back uptown to Oak Street. He checked the numbers. It was three or four blocks before Oak Street crossed with Randall.

As he walked he found his pace slowing with every step. But suddenly, there it was on the next corner, halfway up a lamppost: a white and green sign that read 'Randall Street'.

He quickly checked all four corners, then checked his watch again.

As he watched from the opposite side of the street, one or two people went in and out of Billy's. The light started flashing 'Walk' and he found himself crossing with the other pedestrians.

He checked his watch yet again. Nine minutes to eight. He paused at the doorway of Billy's. Behind the counter was a man stacking some newspapers. He wore a black T-shirt and jeans. He must have been around forty, a shade under six foot, with shoulders that could only have been built by spending several hours a day in the gym.

A customer brushed past Jake and asked for a packet of Marlboros. While the man was handing him his change, Jake stepped into the shop, and pretended to take an interest in the magazine rack.

As the customer turned to leave, Jake slipped his hand into the inside pocket of his jacket. He took out his wallet and touched the edge of the hundred-dollar bill. When the Marlboro man had left the shop, Jake put his wallet back into his pocket, leaving the hundred dollars in the palm of his hand.

The man behind the counter stood waiting impassively

5

as Jake slowly unfolded the bill.

'The *Times*,' Jake heard himself saying, as he placed the hundred-dollar bill on the counter.

The man in the black T-shirt glanced at the note and checked his watch. He seemed to hesitate for a moment before placing his right hand under the counter. Jake tensed at the movement, until he saw a long, thin white envelope emerge. The man proceeded to slip it into the heavy folds of the newspaper's business section, then handed the paper over to Jake, his face still impassive. He took the hundred-dollar bill, rang up seventy-five cents on the cash register, and gave Jake a quarter change. Jake turned and walked quickly out of the shop, nearly knocking over a small man who looked as nervous as Jake felt.

Jake almost ran down Oak Street, glancing back over his shoulder several times to see if anyone was following him. Checking again, he spotted a Yellow Cab, and quickly hailed it.

'The East Side,' he said, jumping in.

As the driver eased back into the traffic, Jake slid the envelope out from the bulky newspaper and transferred it to an inside pocket. He could hear his heart beating. For the next fifteen minutes he could barely take his eyes from the cab's back window.

When he saw a subway coming up on the right, he told the driver to pull into the kerb. He handed over ten dollars, jumped out of the taxi and dashed down the subway steps, emerging a few moments later on the other side of the road. He then hailed another taxi going in the opposite direction. This time he gave the driver his home address. He congratulated himself on his little subterfuge, which he'd seen carried out by Michael Douglas in the Movie of the Week.

Nervously Jake touched his inside pocket to be sure the envelope was still in place. Confident that no one was following him, he no longer bothered to look out of the rear window. He was tempted to check inside the envelope, but there would be time enough to do that once he was back in the safety of his apartment. He checked his watch: 8.21. Ellen and the children wouldn't be home for at least half an hour.

'Another fifty yards on the left,' Jake told the driver, happy to be back on familiar territory. He cast one final glance through the back window as the taxi drew in to the kerb near his block. There was no other traffic to be seen. He paid the driver with the dimes and quarters he had taken from his daughter's Snoopy box, then jumped out and walked as calmly as he could into the building.

Once he was inside, he rushed across the hall and banged the elevator button with the palm of his hand. It still wasn't working. He cursed, and started to run up the seven flights of stairs to his apartment. Breathless, he unbolted the three locks of the front door and slammed it behind him, resting against it while he got his breath back.

He was pulling the envelope out of his inside pocket when the phone began to ring. His first thought was that they had traced him somehow and wanted their money back. He stared at the phone for a moment, then nervously picked up the receiver.

'Hello? Jake, is that you?'

Then he remembered. 'Yes, Mom.'

'You didn't call at six,' she said.

'I'm sorry, Mom. I did, but . . .' He decided against telling her any more.

'I've been trying to get you for the past hour. Have you been out or something?'

'Just to the bar across the road. I sometimes go there for a drink when Ellen takes the kids to the movies.'

He placed the envelope next to the phone, desperate to be rid of her, but aware that he would have to go through the usual Saturday routine.

'Anything interesting in the *Times*, Mom?' he heard himself saying, rather too quickly.

7

'Not much,' she replied. 'Clinton's still saying he didn't do anything wrong. I don't know why I ever voted for the guy.'

'I did tell you not to, Mom,' Jake said, giving his standard reply. He picked up the envelope and squeezed it, testing the feel of a hundred thousand dollars.

'Anything else, Mom?' he threw in.

'There's a piece in the style section about widows of seventy rediscovering their sex drive. As soon as their husbands are safely in their graves it seems they're popping Viagra and getting back into the old routine. One of them's quoted as saying, "I'm not so much trying to make up for lost time, as to catch up with him." '

As he listened, Jake began to ease open a corner of the envelope.

'I'd try it myself,' his mother was saying, 'but I can't afford the facelift that seems to be an essential part of the deal.'

'Mom, I think I can hear Ellen and the kids at the door. I'd better say goodbye. We'll see you at lunch tomorrow.'

'But I haven't told you about a fascinating piece in the business section.'

'I'm listening,' said Jake, slowly beginning to tear the envelope open.

'It's a story about a new scam. I don't know what they'll think of next.'

The envelope was half open.

'It seems that a gang has found a way of tapping into your phone while you're dialling another number . . .'

Another inch and Jake would be able to tip the contents of the envelope out on to the table.

'So when you dial, you think you've got a crossed line.'

Jake dropped the envelope, and began to listen more carefully.

'Then they set you up by making you believe you're listening to a real conversation.'

Sweat began to appear on Jake's forehead as he stared

down at the half-opened envelope.

'During the conversation they make you think that if you travel to the other side of the city and hand over a hundred-dollar bill, you'll get an envelope containing a hundred thousand dollars for it.'

Jake felt sick at the thought of how easily he had parted with his hundred dollars, and how skilfully he had been tricked.

'They're using tobacconists and newsagents to carry out the scam,' continued his mother.

'But what's in the envelope?' demanded Jake.

'Now that's where they're really clever,' said his mother. 'They put a small booklet in it that gives advice on how to make a hundred thousand dollars – so they're not even breaking the law. You've got to hand it to them.'

I already have, Mom, Jake wanted to say, but he just slammed the phone down and stared at the envelope.

The front doorbell began to ring. Ellen and the kids must be back from the movie.

The bell rang again.

'OK, I'm coming, I'm coming,' shouted Jake. He seized the envelope, determined to leave no trace of its embarrassing existence. As the bell rang a third time he looked round the room, then ran into the kitchen, opened the incinerator and threw the envelope in.

The bell rang again. This time the ringer was keeping a finger on the button.

Jake ran to the door, he threw it open, to find three massive men standing in the hallway. The one wearing a black T-shirt put a knife against his throat, while the other two grabbed him. The door slammed shut.

'Where is it?' the man shouted, holding the knife against Jake's throat.

'Where's what?' asked Jake. 'I haven't got anything.'

'Don't play games with us,' shouted the second man. 'We want the envelope with our hundred thousand dollars back.'

9

'But there was no money in it, only a book. I threw it into the incinerator. Listen, you can hear it for yourself.'

The man in the black T-shirt cocked his head, while the other two remained silent. There was a distant roar from the incinerator in the kitchen.

'OK, then, you're going to go the same way,' said the man holding the knife.

Jake could feel its cold edge at his throat. Then the phone and the front doorbell both began ringing at once.

Jeffrey Archer's novels are all published
by HarperCollins.

from The Long Firm
by Jake Arnott

In The Long Firm – *an epic tale of a gangster's rise and fall – high life meets low life and real and imaginary characters spar with each other as the seedy end of the swinging sixties is revealed in ruthless verisimilitude . . .*

The Stardust. Harry was out front, flanked by two huge doormen, greeting people. He grabbed my hand with both of his. Gave me a wink as I passed through into the club.

'Glad you could come, Terry. Get yourself a drink, I'll see you later.'

The Stardust. Not exactly my scene. Mostly an older crowd, overdressed and out of style. Heinz and The Wild Boys were performing that night. I went to the bar and ordered a rum and Coke. A modernist kid to the left of me in a two-piece tonic mohair. Three-buttoned single-breasted jacket, narrow lapels, flap pockets, from Harry Fenton's no doubt. He wore his hair *en brosse*, in a French crew. He nodded at me. I felt shabby standing next to him. I want some of that, I thought to myself. Something more than that.

Bleached-blond Heinz was dragging his backing band through a medley of Eddie Cochran songs.

'Pretty, ain't he?' said the mod kid.

'Yeah,' I shrugged. 'I guess.'

'Shame about the voice. Still, Joe Meek's so in love with him he's convinced he's going to be big.'

He nodded at a tall quiffed man sitting at the main table watching the performance intensely. Joe Meek, record producer, famous for his ice-rink-in-space electric organ sound. He'd had a big hit with 'Telstar' by The Tornadoes.

'Joe should stick to instrumentals,' muttered the modernist as the blond singer crooned 'C'mon Everybody' slightly off key. 'So should Heinz, for that matter.'

Harry had come into the club with his entourage. He beckoned me over with a jerk of his head.

'Come over and join us,' he said and led me to a large table.

The party was an assortment of celebrities. Along with Joe Meek there was a boxer or two, someone from television and Ruby Ryder the film actress. Equally famous and with their own brand of glamour were the people pointed out with names like Alibi Albert and Jack the Hat. 'Faces', Harry referred to them as. And as it turned out that was what Harry was. A face. *Mad* Harry, I was slightly disconcerted to learn, was his also known as. Every so often a flashbulb would go whoosh and the main group would go into a fixed expression for a second. Showbiz eyes and teeth. Underworld jaws and suits.

I was introduced to Joe Meek. Being the official young person present, he was keen for my opinion on Heinz. I hesitated.

'Love the peroxide riah,' I declared with genuine conviction.

'It's great, ain't it?' Joe had a high-pitched west country accent. 'Got the idea from *Village of the Damned*. You know, those spooky kids from outer space.'

He was as tall and thickset as Harry but his movements had a kind of jerky thinness to them. He had big farmboy hands that fluttered at you. I didn't have the heart to tell him that I didn't think Heinz was going to work. The

12

dyed hair, the shiny jacket with silver piping. Wonderfully camp. Woefully out of date. Something new was happening. The Beat Boom, people were calling it. Rock and roll, well, that was for the die-hard leather crowd and Heinz certainly didn't impress them. Apparently in Birmingham a gang of rockers had chucked tins of beans at him. Rhythm and blues, that was what everyone was talking about. Something new was happening but Heinz definitely wasn't it.

Heinz finished to polite applause. He came over to the table grinning awkwardly. Joe fussed around him for a while and then chatted, wide-eyed manic, to Harry. Pupils like sharpened pencil leads. Pilled on amphetamine, no doubt about it. Blocked, we called it.

They talked business. Management. Heinz sat between them and they furtively eyed him like confection as they talked. Harry was drawn to Tin Pan Alley, a way of breaking into legitimate show business. Maybe thinking of becoming the next Larry Parnes or Brian Epstein. And why not? He was a homosexual Jewish wide boy just like them. But maybe a bit too wide. Not quite smooth enough. Harry would never look right in a camel-hair coat somehow. He was too much of a performer to be a successful impresario. You could never see him in the background. Too conspicuous, too much of an act himself. In fact all the faces seemed to have a more confident turn than any of the showbiz lot. The gangsters were the real stars at The Stardust.

I got drunk. I wasn't used to boozing. I staggered into the gents, splashed some cold water in my face and dried it on the towel machine. Jack the Hat was handing over a huge bag of pills to the modernist child.

'Fancy a doob, mate?' he called over to me.

I rejoined the party with a purple heart melting on my tongue. Around the table, stories were being offered up. Showbiz secrets and behind-the-scenes gossip swapped for tales of fixed fights and doped dogs. Frauds and rackets and heavier jobs were alluded to as all the tricks of the trade seemed open for discussion. Like conjurers taking apart an illusion, confident that their public was elsewhere. The audience, the punters. The mugs.

One of the villain's women got up and gave us a song to much encouragement. She had a clear, sad voice. You could see that she had been pretty once but now she looked a bit washed out. As she sang 'Cry Me A River' without accompaniment I wondered what kind of a life it would be being the woman of one of these hard-faced men.

When she'd finished there was applause and banging on the tables. Everyone was far gone by now. Music started up and Jack the Hat got up and danced on the table. I could hear Joe Meek next to me bawling about the record industry in the mod kid's ear over the noise.

'They're trying to steal my sound! The rotten pigs! I'm still the bloody guv'nor!'

Jack the Hat was starting to strip off and two of the boxers tried to gently coax him down off the table. Harry came up and put his arm around me.

'Enjoying yourself?'

I nodded. Actually I was. It wasn't a trendy scene but there was something altogether furtive and exciting about The Stardust. It reminded me of that bit in Pinocchio where all the bad boys bunk off school and go to Playland where they don't have to do any work and can just fuck about all day. As a child I'd always longed for that sort of cheap utopia. When the funfair came to our local common every year, I'd be drawn to the cheap thrills of the waltzer and the dodgems. I spent as much time simply gazing at the gypsy lads as they casually hopped amidst the spinning machinery, collecting fares. Showing off. Danger and glamour. Greased-back pompadours and muscled arms marked with tattoos and stained with engine oil. I'd always fancied the rough boys who ran the fairground rides. The Stardust scene seemed a version of the playland I'd dreamed of as a child and I wanted to be

14

a part of it. I'd conveniently forgotten that, in the story, all the lazy boys are turned into donkeys in the end. I should have been warned.

Anyway, the speed had sobered me up. Given me confidence. When the party was over and people began to stagger out of the club, Harry asked me to go back with him and I said yes.

At the door a bloke in a heavy overcoat came across and muttered something in Harry's ear. They whispered gruffly to each other in the doorway.

'All right, I'll deal with it. Terry,' Harry said, turning to me, 'Jimmy will drive you to my flat. Wait there for me. I won't be long.'

He nodded to a sandy-haired man who was waiting outside. I recognized him as Harry's driver from the night we met at The Casbah. Harry said a few words to him, turned and winked at me and then went off into the night.

From the back of the Daimler I saw Jimmy's eyes slotted in the rear-view mirror.

'All right, son?' he asked with a little nod of the head.

There was a weary edge to his voice.

'Yeah,' I replied. 'I guess.'

Jimmy unlocked the door of the flat and held it open for me. He wrinkled his nose in an obliging sneer.

'Make yourself at home,' he said. 'Harry might be a while.'

Then he was gone and I was alone in Harry's flat.

I poured myself a large brandy and looked through Harry's record collection. Judy Garland, Dorothy Squires, some opera and Winston Churchill's Wartime Speeches. On the coffee table was *A History of Western Philosophy* by Bertrand Russell and a well-thumbed edition of *Physique Pictorial*. I collapsed into the leather-buttoned chesterfield and flicked through the magazine. The speed had begun to wear off and I started to feel drowsy from the brandy. A second glass sorted me out and I fell into a light sleep on the sofa.

I woke up with a start to find Harry standing over me still in his overcoat. He prodded me gently with his foot.

'All right?' he whispered.

He had a slightly crazed look about him. His face twitched with the strange distracted playfulness that a cat displays when it's just killed a mouse.

'Where have you been?' I asked, rubbing my face awake.

'Shh,' Harry ordered with a finger in front of his mouth. 'Never you mind.'

I sat up and he grinned at me.

'Come on,' he said softly, taking my arm and leading me into the bedroom.

The Long Firm *by Jake Arnott will be published by Hodder & Stoughton.*

from E/P

by David Baddiel
Extract from a work in progress

E/P is the second novel (after the bestselling Time For
Bed*) by TV writer and performer David Baddiel. It
opens on the day of Princess Diana's death, and is a
tragicomic and very contemporary romance sparked by
witty dialogue.*

Vic fucked her first the day Princess Diana died. He'd
thought of the sympathy scenario before, of course, some
heavy issue she might come to him with that he could
turn round, problems with Joseph, her mother's illness
going terminal, whatever. But Emma, round about then,
she was a problem-free zone; even given her mother's
condition, you could bank on her chipperness, always
opening the door looking like she'd just been laughing,
her face still crinkled with pleasure at some joke now gone
into the untellable ether. So he thought of it, that trans-
mission, such a short move, the conciliatory arm over the
shoulder going down a touch, to touch, or better still a
hug, which when you move apart from, your faces are
close enough . . . he thought of it, but it was never top of
his list of probables because she was never sad.

And then bang! Sunday, 31 August 1997. At 8.30 Tess
woke him up, calling from Paris. She'd been on the
night-time train from Marseilles, getting back from a
tasting – this shipment, she'd said, was going to crack the

market, she'd found some nondescript vineyard in the south where the bottles were like Lafite, only one-tenth of the cost – when a gendarme, a proper Peter Sellers – give his hat a neck-hanky and he's in the Foreign Legion, 'tache and everything – raps smartly, raps like in a film, on the *compartement* door. Bleary-eyed, probably hung-over – Tess never spat out as much as she should – Vic's wife rolled over and, without getting off her top couchette, slid the glass to the left, a tumble-haired woman in a T-shirt saying, 'I hate the Pixies,' probably not the image the gendarme had in his mind when he made the decision to alert the English passengers of the terrible news.

'*Vous-êtes anglaise?*' he said, urgently, snapping with import.

'*Oui . . .*' says Tess, squinting against the white backlighting him against the carriage window.

A pause; a breath. '*Lady Diana* (so many people said that: *Lady* Diana. So ingrained, whatever you are first called) *est morte!*'

Another pause, but this time filled with nothing, a not knowing what to say or do. They looked at each other for a while, and then Tess told Vic she said, 'Um . . . *Merci.*' And slid back the glass door.

They laughed, at the gendarme, at the idea of him standing crestfallen outside the door, maybe staying there for a while uncertainly, before pulling himself together and moving on to the next *compartement*, in the hope of the news being taken by those passengers with a greater sense of historical moment. And then Tess said she'd decided to stay in Paris for a couple of days because England was going to go crazy.

Vic spent that Sunday doing what you did. He watched TV all day, looking, looking, for increasing moistness in Martyn Lewis's eyes, for evidence of conspiracy, for more news when there was none. He sat in a big chair in their small flat, high above Sydenham Hill, and overdosed on the death of Di. He wasn't thinking about Em at all, much, except maybe to ring and talk to her or Joe about it, that'd be a new vein to puncture in the feeding of this novel craving, and then the phone went and it was her.

'Hi,' she said, and straightaway he could hear the struggle, the getting through the lump it took even to say that small syllable.

'Hi. You OK?'

'Uh . . . not really. Can I come round?'

Funny, but he didn't think why she might be upset. He didn't know then that people, actual people, would be devastated, that all their griefs were going to get parcelled up in this one big one; and so he just thought 'What's wrong?' but didn't say it, because already his possibility fire had been lit.

'Yeah, sure. I'm going to be in all day.'

Vic liked it when you knew that about days.

When Vic opened the door and saw her looking all snuffly and red-eyed and definitely not crinkled up from some recent Joe joke, she said to him, 'God, Vic, have you been crying?'

He hadn't, not at all. One or two of the hastily-put-together montages to music, yes, he'd let them through, more to feel something different, to shift the cold fascination to something else, pity, maybe. But crying, no.

What he did have was hay fever. It lasted really long that summer, starting in early May with the first phase, the ticklish stuff just behind your face, controllable with antihistamines, and then in mid-June the second phase, a whole new set of pollens blown in from the fields, which turn your skull to water, and which no pill or spray or potentially lethal injection can stem. By September, though, the dandelion clouds are normally on their way, and if the streets are full in an Indian summer, it's liable to be hay feverites, trying desperately to enjoy the weather the one time they can. But that year, for some reason, maybe because summer came not at all in July and only haltingly in August, the pollen hung in there, and there were still days in September when Vic's nose was a snot volcano. On the 2nd, it was mainly his eyes, so itchy his index fingers were in a permanent crook ready for the next rub.

Now, Vic had had hay fever since before he knew what it was, and he hated it, he hated it with menaces and outrage, this recurring inner rash, this thing with no upside, no redeeming features whatsoever, not like some allergies (yeast: good for dieting; antibiotics: good for forcing doctors to give you unusual drugs – Vic knew a bloke who was allergic to pickles, it meant that McDonald's had to hand-cook his burgers, how special must that make you feel) but suddenly, for the first time in twenty-eight years, he saw a way of turning it to his advantage.

'Might have been,' he said, with an approximation of a watery smile.

'Oh *Vic*,' she said, and crumpled, like the zones of that car, into him.

Straight afterwards, lying in bed with her head full of sleep trusting on his chest, his first fear was how to keep up the tearful aspect, the crying eyes, what with the fading bloom of summer and all; he'd want it to last as long as the desire did. But then God smiled in Vic's direction, oh, what a big Teletubbies sun-baby grin it was, and covered London for him in a carpet of flowers.

E/P *by David Baddiel will be published
by Little, Brown.*

from Hens Dancing

by Raffaella Barker

Raffaella Barker has been described as 'one of the cleverest and freshest young British novelists' (Daily Mail). *In* Hens Dancing *she brings us a tale of the* vie de bohème *in rural Norfolk which will win the hearts of readers everywhere.*

April 26th

Spring pours in through every window on a tide of blossom-scented air. One of the hens, Custard, or perhaps Flustered, has hatched three chicks and they bowl about after her, tiny blobs of apricot cotton wool beneath the apple blossom. The Beauty is very taken with them and makes her way towards the orchard any time she is not under close surveillance. Her new shuffle, on her bottom with rowing action from her legs, is speedy, and I am constantly having to leave the telephone dangling from its rubber spiral, or damp laundry spewing from the washing machine, to follow her as she scoops herself down the drive with Rags. Giles offers to look after her this morning, but becomes engrossed in *Billy Whizz*; The Beauty eats three geranium heads and is sick.

'She's been sick, Mum.' Giles wanders off, reminding me unpleasantly of his father. The Beauty takes advantage and vanishes. This time I discover her with Felix. He is attempting to climb a small flowering tree with her, but has not yet got far up it. He is doing well. The Beauty is wedged into a fork in the branches and squeals and claps with delight as Felix climbs up past her then reaches down to lift her on to her next perch. There she rests, a vision of rustic charm, in her green jersey with ladybirds on it, waving a fat hand at me from behind a spray of apple blossom.

Mustard the cockerel is in attendance. He is a control freak and polices the garden daily to make sure that all is as it should be. He likes to find The Beauty in her pram under a tree, and hops on to the handle to cast a beady eye over her as she sleeps. Sometimes he cannot resist spoiling everything, and crows mightily from this vantage point, startling The Beauty awake and causing her to yell. This morning he is not pleased to find her flitting about in treetops, and perches himself at a cautious distance on the swing to watch while emitting a ghastly slow groaning noise.

April 29th

What was to have been a lazy Monday morning due to the boys having the day off, is shattered by the shrilling of the doorbell and pounding on the door at seven-fifteen. It is David Lanyon and two carbuncled henchmen, one with a bobble hat, one without.

'Hi, I hope you don't mind, I've brought Digger.' He gestures towards the garden where a muscular black Labrador is aiming a jet of steaming urine at my green tulips. David is a shining example of health, optimism and clean laundry; he has on a washed-out red guernsey and jeans faded to the point that I always long for mine to reach. He chats to the boys, who are hanging around in the hall in their pyjamas. Giles and Felix bond with him instantly.

22

'Mum, have you seen David's trainers? They're excellent. Can I have some?' His helpers are less fragrant, and look like a couple of Scaven Dwarves from *War Hammer*. I begin to feel utterly invaded as they tramp in and out with toothy saws, rolls of cable and sagging metal toolboxes. David's car, an old Red Cross Land Rover with logo still intact, is reversed right up to the door to speed the unloading process. The postman arrives, and even though he only has one thin card reminding me of The Beauty's vaccination dates and the door is wide open, he finds it necessary to ring the bell and express concern.

'Hope nobody's been badly hurt,' he says, and I smile as disdainfully as I can with sheepskin slippers, bare legs and a helping of Ready Brek plastered over my shoulders.

'Not yet, but that may change.' My taut, brooding delivery is faultless, and he drives off very alarmed.

Later

The bathroom is a cross between a potential Little Mermaid's sea palace and Stig's dump. Sticks of MDF and little piles of sawdust lie among the stacks of castellated wood and odd lengths of gleaming copper piping. Plastic tubes, sand, insulating foam and baskets of mottled shells fill every spare inch, and there is no way anyone will be able to use the room for at least a week.

The two Dwarf Warriors have gone, David is teaching Giles and Felix how to slow-bowl on the lawn and The Beauty is having her bath in the kitchen sink. This is huge fun. She puts a green flannel on her head and delivers her mad, squeaky laugh. As I lift her out, Digger trots past the window with a blur of feathers in his mouth. Wild rage surges. I scream, 'You bloody bastard shithead dog.' The Beauty's face crumples and her mouth becomes a square of misery.

Am heading out to kill Digger when Giles runs in,

23

breathless. 'Don't worry Mum, it isn't a hen. It's a pheasant from the meadow, David just got it with Felix's catapult. It was such a cool shot, I wish you'd seen it.'

I joggle The Beauty about and she begins to coo again, so sanity can now return. 'How did you know what I was thinking?'

Giles giggles, 'We could hear you swearing from the other side of the garden. You must have left The Beauty's intercom on outside. David said I should run and tell you before you burst a blood vessel.'

'What a disgusting image.' I turn crossly and flounce upstairs to give The Beauty her bottle. When I come down half an hour later, Giles and Felix are watching a video of *Calamity Jane* and David has gone. I settle down on the sofa in time to sing along with Doris Day to 'Take Me Back to the Black Hills of Dakota'.

May 1st

Dawn finds me crawling around in the garden with bits of wet grass on my face, having washed it in dew for increased possibility of great beauty. This is an economy drive, and virtue propels me about beneath the apple trees which are bowing and quivering in arctic winds. I could be paying large sums of money to a mail-order beauty company whose boast is that their products 'give the complexion the glow of a country walk, the texture of a sun-drenched apricot'. I can't wait to achieve this loveliness, and am convinced that nature can do as well as agnès b. in assisting me.

May Day is traditionally riven with ice storms and hailstones of record-breaking proportions and today is no different. I do not linger in the orchard, but dash inside to a mirror. A red nose and mud-strewn cheeks are the only sign that I have been involved in a beauty treatment, otherwise the usual pallor prevails. My skin looks nothing like a sun-drenched apricot: the economical rustic beauty treatment is wanting. But I did try. Virtuously, I write a plump cheque to agnès b. and post it off. Within twenty-eight days I will achieve the longed-for apricot look with the assistance of Super Silk tinted moisturizer. Until then I shall avoid being seen in strong sunlight. Pretty easy, if this freakish and foul weather continues.

May 3rd

Terrible cabin fever this week, caused by the work in the bathroom. All day drills whine, saws rasp and hammers bang until I am forced out into the garden to escape. Have therefore achieved a lot of weeding and no work. Weeding is second only to hanging the washing out in my tally of chores that give job satisfaction. For me, the washing line is as good as any piece of contemporary art. Indeed, when married I could always irritate Charles a lot by telling friends of my plan to take a washing machine, a line, some pegs and a few days' laundry down to Cork Street and set myself up as a one-woman show. I still think it's a good idea, and often expand my thesis. A narrative statement could so easily be found in the separation of whites (innocence) and darks (death). The coloured wash can represent anything – sin, love, family life, fertility or joy; even a disaster such as colours running can be turned on its head so that all the grey vests symbolise politics or our cultural identity or something similar.

Whenever I start thinking about this again I am reminded what a brilliant idea it is. Promise myself that tomorrow I shall take photographs of my washing line and send them to Charles Saatchi.

Increasingly, planning and fantasy are replacing any social life in the evenings. It is six months since Charles lived here, and even then he was only around at weekends because in the week he was in Cambridge at the head office of Heavenly Petting. I realize, with horror, that I am no longer civilized. Have not spent ordinary, companionable evenings with a husband or similar creature for years. I don't know how to any more. Quickly telephone Rose to discover what she is doing now, it being mid-evening. Reassuringly, she is eating Twiglets and will be having cereal to follow. Tristan is apparently watching a programme about war and weaponry and has not said a word to her since he came home from work.

'Have you had a row?'

'Oh, no, he just doesn't speak most of the time.'

'Have you fed him?'

'He made himself a foul-looking jam and peanut butter sandwich and then said he didn't want any supper.' She yawns. 'I'm going to bed now, actually; Theo is getting more teeth so I'm bound to have a bad night with him. Let's speak tomorrow when they're all out of the way.'

It does not sound like much of an improvement on my evening. Immeasurably cheered, I ring off and get back to my plans for the laundry exhibition.

Hens Dancing *by Raffaella Barker is published*
by Review.

Old Smokeytoes

by Louis de Bernières

Louis de Bernières' South American trilogy, starting with The War of Don Emmanuel's Nether Parts, *established him as a young author to watch. His fourth novel,* Captain Corelli's Mandolin, *was published to extraordinary acclaim, and has become a huge international bestseller.*

I dreamed recently that I was a highly successful person, but that someone had placed a kipper beneath my toupee as I slept, so that for months everybody avoided me as though I were a bearer of the plague. I cannot explain the desperation of my loneliness and incomprehension, for I was unable to detect the rank stench owing to the fact that my nose had disingenuously adapted itself to detect every aroma except my own. 'Why didn't you feel the decaying fish under your wig?' I hear you inquire, and 'Didn't you see it when you took your hairpiece off?' and I reply 'For God's sake, this was a dream, and dreams don't have to make much sense.' It's enough that they're erotic, or terrifying, or arrestingly peculiar. They have their own perverse logic, and that is why I did not appreciate that there was a fish under my toupee until I woke up. I sat up in my bed and clutched at my head in an ecstasy of humiliation and embarrassment, only to realize abruptly that I wasn't bald and had never worn a toupee in my life.

There was therefore no possibility of a smoked herring finding itself on or about my person. Nonetheless, it took some moments before my heart settled down and my panic subsided. I suppose that I might have dreamed about kippers because my slumbering and snorting spouse takes spoonfuls of cod-liver oil after our bath and before our bed, gleefully aware, one presumes, that the resulting halitosis is an excellent prophylactic against amorous advances. They say that no man is respected by his valet, and equally I might add that no dictator is respected by his wife. Hence the unregrettable necessity of mistresses.

There is probably some elaborate Freudian explanation for this dream, but I must suppose that in fact it merely lays bare my eternal suspicion that I was born to fail even though I appear to be at the apogee of perpetual success. Great men have always borne inside them the germ of their own destruction, and in my case it would appear to consist of a fatal lack of complete confidence in myself. I have always given the impression of perfectly crisp command and lucid clarity of purpose but, even when I am on the balcony and below me a delirious crowd applauds my every word, I have never been able to forget that I am merely mortal and that one day I might make a mistake. I feel that perhaps I have failed to develop that sense of personal godhead which so sustained Hitler, or the Roman emperors.

One cannot, however, become a dictator without developing an acute sense of mortality. Common people detest success, and would conspire to bring one down even if one gave them their heart's desire on a daily and ever more generous basis, and moreover one gathers enemies as a squirrel gathers nuts. I trod on a large number of sensitive toes in order to come to rule this country, and I have had to stove in a lot of hard skulls in order to preserve my position.

In one sense it was ludicrously easy. All you have to do

is stir up nationalism, and cultivate a frenzy of hatred against any group of people that takes your fancy. I decided against Jews, because that was old hat, and went for blacks instead. I know that this was not very original either, and nowadays I most poignantly wish that I had picked something a little more startling, perhaps even a little whimsical. Cat-lovers, homosexual poets, postmodernists, that kind of thing.

But blacks it was, and of course I do not need to go into the details of the things I did, because they are already world-famous, or notorious, depending upon your point of view. So famous, or notorious, that I became automatically and *de rigueur* the target of black and integrationist assassination plots from all around the world. This is one reason why I sometimes wish I had not chosen blacks; I cannot imagine cat lovers sending me gifts of exploding cigars, or homosexual poets springing from the palace rhododendrons armed with a machete. I especially cannot imagine a postmodernist being capable of coming up with anything interesting.

For a while the attempted assassinations greatly increased my popularity with the general population, so much so that fairly regularly I had them faked, but I have to say that eventually they began to fray my nerves. I would jump out of my skin every time a door slammed, and many of life's mundane pleasures lost their charm. For example, if an admirer sent me a chocolate cake, I would not be able to eat it in case it was poisoned. My staff would guzzle it, of course, and afterwards I would be left feeling quite wistful. I began to feel persecuted, and to realize why so many great dictators finally became paranoid. One might as well dress up as an antelope and invite a pride of lions to dinner; it is an entirely thankless task, except when one is thanked by a sycophant, whose thanks one would rather not have had in any case.

But now I have very real grounds for paranoia, and I can see that finally I am going to have to go.

It is not merely that I lost the lower parts of both legs in the explosion. That was certainly bad enough, and I still wonder how I managed to run the country from my sickbed when I was either wild with pain or sedated up to my eyebrows. Moreover I had recurrent nightmares, even whilst wide awake, in which I stood once again upon the podium addressing the Mothers of the National Purification, only to be launched suddenly upon a terrifyingly bewildering and seemingly endless parabola. I crash abruptly back to earth amid a painful storm of planks and splinters, and when I attempt to stand, discover that I no longer have the means to do so. I experience all over again the sensation of perfect horror that leaves the stomach aching like a void, and I hear the wails and shrieks of the assembled Mothers, whose faces are blackened by soot and whose respectable but anachronistic hats are missing or askew.

It is certainly true that, just as was trumpeted by the national press, the transplant was a complete success. Indeed, the nation now sees its leader striding about as if nothing had ever happened, a wonderful tribute both to the supreme skill of the surgeons and my own fabled toughness. 'The Indestructible' was added to my imposing list of titles, honorifics, and sobriquets.

Unfortunately 'The Refuted' should have been added as well, for I am now not only three centimetres taller, but I am also a black man from both knees downwards. For weeks I was told by the surgeon that this was simply post-operational trauma and bruising that would eventually disappear, and by the time that the appalling truth finally sank in, the new parts were perfectly fused into position and the surgical team had fled joyously to France where the story had been sold to *Paris Match* for a most considerable sum.

It appeared that the black man whose lower legs were now my own means of transport had been the victim of one of my Experimentation and Extermination Squads, and that his fresh remains had been delivered in ice to the hospital. The surgeons discovered that the tissue was a perfect match with mine, and it occurred to them that it would be fabulously and amusingly apposite to prove upon my own person that my racial doctrines were absolutely false. After all, every schoolboy knows that the tissues of differing species cannot possibly be grafted together.

I had known perfectly well, and all along, that my propaganda was balderdash, and I had only propounded it in order to consolidate the nation behind me. I admit to a certain cynicism; cynicism is a prerequisite of intelligent dictatorship. But I had not expected to be so dramatically and ironically confounded, and nor so publicly, for it was quite impossible for me to prevent the news from spreading like wildfire from France. In the modern world communications are regrettably instantaneous and uncontrollable. As is humour; it was not long before every public lavatory in the land was covered with cartoons of me in my uniform with the trouser legs rolled up, and the feet and shins shaded in black. The country rapidly became ungovernable, and Intelligence sources revealed that my nickname had been changed from an affectionate 'The Old Man' to a derisive 'Old Smokeytoes'. It took no great acuity to perceive that even my wife and my own most loyal staff were sniggering behind my back, and I began to receive invitations from swimming clubs and naturist colonies.

I have decided that the nation's gift to me upon my unexpected retirement early tomorrow shall be a nice little island in the Adriatic. I have already bought it with funds diverted from the Ministry of Racial Harmony.

It has just occurred to me that the kipper in my recurring nightmare probably symbolizes my Negro legs. I suppose that the toupee must symbolize my trousers. But what was the stench that everyone but myself could smell?

All Louis de Bernières' novels are published by Vintage Press.

from The Consolations of Philosophy

by Alain de Botton

Alain de Botton was born in 1969. He is the author of
Essays in Love, The Romantic Movement, Kiss and
Tell *and* How Proust can Change Your Life. *His work
is translated into sixteen languages.*

Montaigne and his Books

It may be useful to feel stupid. Few historical ages have
drawn more benefit from their sense of intellectual inferi-
ority than the early Renaissance. The first half of the
sixteenth century was marked by a revival of interest in,
and deference towards, the wisdom of Ancient Greece
and Rome. Among the intellectual élites of Europe, a
consensus emerged that the finest thinking the world had
yet witnessed had occurred amongst a handful of geniuses
in the Italian peninsula and the city states of Greece
between the construction of the Parthenon and the sack
of Rome – and that there was no greater scholarly priority
than to recover their works and disseminate them to the
widest audience. There were new editions of Plato,
Aristotle, Catullus, Longinus, Lucretius, Seneca and
Cicero. In France, the new knowledge did not remain
cloistered in the universities. Plutarch's *Lives* and *Moral
Works* were translated into vivid French, and selections
from the classics spread into studies across the land.

In a chateau on a vine-covered hill thirty miles east of Bordeaux lived a man who knew and loved the classics. Michel de Montaigne had been initiated from an early age. He had been taught Latin as a first language; by the age of seven or eight he had read Ovid's *Metamorphoses*; before he was sixteen he had bought a complete set of Virgil and knew intimately the *Aeneid*, Terence, Plautus and the *Commentaries* of Caesar. He spent much of his day in his library, on the third floor of a tower at one end of the chateau. It had three windows, a desk, a fireplace and, arranged on five sets of shelves in a semi-circle, a thousand books of philosophy, history, poetry and religion.

Montaigne's debt to reading was enormous; books were the great solace of his life:

> [Reading] consoles me in my old age and in my retreat; it relieves me of the weight of distressing idleness and, at any time, can rid me of boring company. It blunts the stabs of pain whenever pain is not too overpowering and extreme. To distract me from morose thoughts, I simply need to have recourse to a book.

But despite these signs of bookishness, Montaigne repeatedly stressed the limits of his interest. His *Essays* were peppered with confessions of literary inadequacy; he got bored with what he was reading, he had to skip chapters he couldn't understand, he could gaze blankly into space for hours, he forgot what he'd read only a few minutes before. 'I cannot have lengthy commerce with books,' he explained, and in his fifties realized it had been 'twenty years since I spent one full hour at a time on one book'. He avoided reading anything too complicated ('I only like pleasurable easy books which tickle my interest') and quickly gave up when the argument was hard to follow:

> I am not prepared to bash my brains for anything,
> not even for learning's sake however precious it may
> be. From books all I seek is to give myself pleasure by
> an honourable pastime . . . If I come across difficult
> passages in my reading I never bite my nails over
> them: after making a charge or two I let them be . . .
> If one book wearies me I take up another.

Which was nonsense, or rather playful posturing on the
part of a man with a thousand volumes on his shelf and
an encyclopedic knowledge of Greek and Latin philosophy. If Montaigne exaggerated his laziness, enjoyed pre-
senting himself as a dim gentleman prone to fall asleep
during philosophical expositions, it was disingenuity with
a purpose. The repeated declarations of laziness and
slowness were tactical ways to undermine what
Montaigne took to be a corrupt understanding of intelligence. Running through the *Essays* was an attempt to revise
the dominant criteria used to identify a clever person.

In the traditional humanist framework, intelligent people
were expected to be widely read, to know how to spell, to
understand Greek and Latin, to have a large vocabulary, to
be patient with books, and to quote accurately from ancient
sources – and the education system was designed with the
inculcation of these intellectual virtues in mind. Montaigne disagreed. He had been sent to the most renowned
school in Gascony, the Collège de Guyenne in Bordeaux,
but by the time he left (completing a twelve-year course in
seven), he had learned nothing that would subsequently be
of use to him in the practical conduct of his life.

> I gladly come back to the theme of the absurdity of
> our education: its end has not been to make us good
> and wise but learned. And it has succeeded. It has
> not taught us to seek virtue and to embrace wisdom:
> it has impressed upon us their derivation and their
> etymology.

The purpose of learning and books was not to fill our minds with facts. It was *to teach us how to live*. Wisdom and virtue were Montaigne's educational ideals. Books had to help us understand ourselves, they should impart lessons in how to survive a failed love affair, how to confront death, how to quell our wilder ambitions, how to appease our melancholy or our physical discomforts.

Every difficult book presents us with a choice of whether to judge the author inept for not being clear, or ourselves stupid for not grasping what is going on. Because many important subjects present challenges to the intellect, it is natural for an association to develop in our minds between what is valuable and what is difficult. But this respect may slip into a degenerate belief that the obscurity of books is invariably connected to their profundity – an application in the intellectual sphere of the same perverse mechanism which, in emotional life, leads the mysterious and elusive to gain our respect in a way that the amicable and reliable rarely do.

If Montaigne claimed to be too indolent to understand many books, it was to suggest that there were no legitimate reasons why books in the humanities should be difficult, that the subject matter of philosophy – unlike that of medicine or astronomy – did not require the specialized vocabulary or syntax that render works impassable to lay readers. Montaigne was blaming himself as a reader more saliently to critique scholars as writers. Behind an incomprehensible prose style might lie a desire to escape the effort of writing clearly. What reads easily was rarely so written. Or else it could mask an absence of content, for being complicated offers unparalleled protection against having nothing to say.

Most philosophers aim at being hard to understand. Why? [Because] difficulty is a coin which the learned conjure with, so as not to reveal the vanity of their studies and which human stupidity is keen to accept in payment.

Philosophers had no reason to use words that would sound out of place in the street or market:

> Just as in dress it is the sign of a petty mind to seek to draw attention by some personal or unusual fashion, so too in speech; the search for new expressions and little-known words derives from an adolescent schoolmasterish ambition. If only I could limit myself to words used in Les Halles in Paris.

But writing with simplicity requires courage, for there's a danger one will be overlooked, dismissed as simple-minded by those who consider impassable prose to be the hallmark of intelligence. Montaigne's work can be read as a plea to take others seriously even when their language is unintimidating and their ideas clear – and, by extension, to refrain from considering ourselves as fools if, by virtue of a hole in our education, our own vocabulary happens to be no larger than that of a lettuce stallholder in Les Halles.

Hand in hand with a devaluation of traditional sources of wisdom came praise of some radical alternatives. Many animals were wiser than books, said Montaigne. There were goats who could pick out dittany from a million other plants when they were wounded by spears, tortoises who knew how to hunt for origanum when they had been bitten by vipers, and storks who could give themselves salt-water enemas. In their behaviour, dogs suggested a perfect understanding of dialectical reasoning.

Montaigne mentioned a dog who had been looking for his master and had come upon a three-pronged fork in the road. He had first looked down one road, then another, and then had run down the third after concluding that his master must have travelled down it.

Here was pure dialectic: the dog made use of disjunctive and copulative propositions and adequately enumerated the parts. Does it matter whether he learned all this from himself or from the Dialectica of George of Trebizond?

Animals were even capable of falling in love, and displayed great loyalty and erotic imaginativeness. An elephant had fallen in love with a beautiful woman working as a flower-seller in Alexandria, read Montaigne. When being led through the market, the elephant picked up fruit for her and knew how to slip his trunk through her neckband and agilely massage her breasts. The Greek philosopher Pyrrho, caught on a ship during a fierce storm, told those who were panicking to imitate the example of a very wise pig on board. He was sitting in one corner completely unconcerned with the tempest, in a state of fatalistic, thought-free calm.

Dare we conclude that the benefit of reason (which we praise so highly and on account of which we esteem ourselves to be lords and masters of all creation) was placed in us for our torment? What use is knowledge if, for its sake, we lose the calm and repose which we should enjoy without it and if it makes our condition worse than that of Pyrrho's pig?

Books should be used with care.

The Consolations of Philosophy *by Alain de Botton will be published by Hamish Hamilton.*

from The Spiritual Tourist
by Mick Brown

Mick Brown was born in London in 1950. He is a freelance journalist and broadcaster. He has written two previous books. The Spiritual Tourist *is a timely and idiosyncratic voyage of discovery as we head for the new millennium.*

Happiness cannot be pursued. You do not find happiness; happiness finds you. It is not an end in itself, but a by-product of other activities, often arriving when it is least expected. You can be sitting in the best restaurant, wearing the finest clothes, surrounded by the most dazzling company, safe in the knowledge all your bills are paid, and you may still not be happy. And you can be standing at the kitchen sink, hands in washing-up water, with nowhere to go, and suddenly realize that you feel as happy as you've ever felt in your life. What Connolly calls *Angst* are the small, incremental uncertainties about our place in the scheme of things, the nagging sense that life could somehow be better, if only, if only . . . what? It is the restlessness of self. And yet the very word – happiness – suggests something ephemeral, caught on the wing, no sooner ensnared than it slips from our grasp. To try to make happiness our property, to own it, is to lose it.

So what, then, is permanent?

I am at a funeral of a good man, a Roman Catholic,

loved by his family and friends, who has lived a life of demonstrable kindness and virtue, who has lived by the tenets of his faith. Amid the displays of grief around me, one person alone is not crying. It is the man's wife, whose face is graced with a look of perfect serenity, of acceptance of the fact of her husband's death, and of a certainty that he has taken his place in heaven and that, in the fullness of time, she will be reunited with him there. Blessed assurance. I am in awe of her trust in the beneficence of God, in awe of her faith. How do you explain such faith; how do you find it?

I have received no epiphany to give me faith. I know of people who have heard the voice of God, or been brushed by the wings of angels. I am not among them.

The Spiritual Tourist *by Mick Brown was published by Bloomsbury.*

from The Modern Library

by Carmen Callil and Colm Tóibín

The Modern Library is a vibrant and emphatic celebration of the art of reading and the great discoveries that can be made with literature. Always engaging and thought-provoking, passionately idiosyncratic, it is the perfect book for readers of any age.

Books such as this often come with a daunting or gloomy introduction in which the condition of the novel is put under a microscope. Is the novel read? Is the novel dead? Has anything worthy been written since Austen, Dickens, Melville, Joyce? How can the novel compete with satellite and cable television, video, film, CD-ROM, the Internet, sport, pop music and other forms of what is known as mass culture? We live today, in the famously miserable words of the American critic Harold Bloom, in the 'Age of Resentment' in which 'devoted and solitary readers are now necessarily beleaguered': culture is in irretrievable decline, the romance of reading gone forever. We think otherwise. Merchants of cultural doom are hostile to change. We are not: we embrace it, were brought up with it, wallow in it rather, fighting political correctness with one paw, and gloomy ideologies with the other.

Enthusiasm is the driving force of *The Modern Library*. Its purpose is to celebrate the writers we have loved best, and to proselytize on behalf of their novels: sources of entertainment and enjoyment as satisfying as any computer game, football match, pop video or Hollywood movie. The novel uniquely includes the seductive capacity to explain, to challenge and to experiment with human experience. The novel tells stories to the human race: a basic instinct, a basic need.

We have recommended 194 novels, not for their academic interest or their illustration of the theory of the death of the author, but for precisely the opposite reason – for their illustration of the very life of the author, the power of the live voice, the passion to tell a story, to invent characters and find a form.

Over the past fifty years the map of the novel has changed. There are countries where English is seen as both a plague inflicted on the natives and at the same time as a language which the natives have come to possess more sonorously than the English themselves. In this way, we have studied the novel in English, not the English novel. And so, here is a choice from India, Pakistan, New Zealand, England, Ireland, Scotland, the USA, Australia, Canada, Africa, the Caribbean, Hong Kong, and more.

An example of the joy to be found in this worldwide flowering of the novel in English is the sheer pleasure of coming across, say, the fiction of modern India in which all the familiar narrative genius of the traditional novel – the eighteenth-century confessional novel, the nineteenth-century Dickensian novel – is completely transformed into a vehicle for dramatizing the sprawl, variety and sense of infinite possibility which is modern India. At the other end of the scale, the Scottish novel in the 1980s and 1990s has become a sharp weapon in the battle for Scottish identity and autonomy.

The period from 1950 is characterized by a change in those who wrote and read fiction too. Women have moved to the centre of the novel, so that if you look at the list we have made today and compare it with the choice from the first half of the century, the new power of women as writers is obvious. This power is not entirely new. Anyone who has read the works of Jane Austen and looks then at the work of Penelope Fitzgerald, Ivy Compton Burnett, Elizabeth Taylor, Elizabeth Jolley, will notice a definite continuity of tone and theme, and the abiding presence of wit.

Another reason for this book is to re-emphasize the novelist as a person who, however disagreeable in real life, performs a function which is as essential to the soul of every community as the secret conscience of the tribe. Some of us live in societies in which their governments support and celebrate sportsmen and women, film stars and opera singers and ignore more or less completely their writers. This is particularly true of England and the USA, where the gap between those who are aware of their literary inheritance and those who are not is uncomfortably large. Much of this is to do with the influence of class in the English educational system. Other countries are different. In societies such as Ireland or Scotland the novel has come to fill in certain gaps, spaces between the public and private, and the novelist – whether he or she likes it or not – has seemed to strengthen a fragile identity. In Nigeria, the novelist has become a dangerous opposition to those in power. In Canada, they only produce geniuses. In other societies where whole communities have been marginalized and impoverished the novel has yet to enter its heroic phase.

What we noticed and appreciated in the books we chose is the sense of the individual voice at work, and sometimes at play, the individual will, the individual choice, the individual talent, the direct relationship between the writer and the reader. (No wonder governments are suspicious of writers.) But there are fascinating national myths and mores, aspects of heritage and history, to which many writers subscribe. It is, of course, not possible to talk about a National Style for novelists, but some themes have endured. For example, from the Indian novels chosen you will learn a great deal about Partition, the British Raj, the caste system, and the influence of mass poverty and religion on India; there are a good number of novels on the list about racial tension in the United States (Morrison, Doctorow); other Americans, men only, attempt a sweeping, ambitious history, as though no other version existed (Pynchon, DeLillo); other Americans manage to dramatize the individual's isolation, eccentricity and sense of not being part of the official version (Flannery O'Connor, Edmund White). In Africa, the conflict between colonized and colonizer remains a theme which no one can escape. In Ireland, the Troubles haunt some contemporary writing but then other work (Beckett) refuses to deal with it and becomes all the richer and stranger for that.

While we differ in our response to literary theory – one of us is hostile to it, while the other cannot have enough of it – we were as one in our determination to ignore the division between so-called 'popular fiction' and 'literary fiction' (also so-called). This false division, which is prevalent in literary pages, in literary prizes, in academia and in our educational mores, has been treacherously responsible for the suggestion that reading is a chore, and that the best writing is always difficult and obscure.

For us, the debate whether Anne Rice's *Interview with the Vampire* is of greater intrinsic merit than Evelyn Waugh's Sword of Honour trilogy is irrelevant, because any decision on the subject – and a decision can be made – alters not at all the fact that both are splendid feats of the human imagination, explains nothing of the pleasure experienced as the novelist's imagination locks into that of the reader, but simply reveals a great deal about those arguing. The critical dividing line between 'popular' and 'literary' also ignores the reader and the writer, who rarely contemplate the novel in this way.

Any list like this is entirely personal but in every choice

we've looked for the same quality – a certain (or sometimes even an uncertain) genius in the work and a certain (always certain) excitement in the reading and the feeling that you would love to hand this book to someone else to read. Most of us, these days, are almost imprisoned by choice, as anyone examining the fiction shelves of a large bookshop will notice. We have used our prejudices and preferences to cut a path through this rich jungle, always using as our final point of judgement that touch of genius and sense of excitement which connects Patrick White with Ruth Rendell, Georgette Heyer with Don DeLillo, J.D. Salinger with Irvine Welsh.

We have chosen these novels for readers, readers of every age and taste, for those who have never read a novel before and for experts who want to quarrel with our choice; for school students and undergraduates, grandfathers, priests, nuns and Antarctic explorers. There are short novels, and long novels – each kind providing a different kind of pleasure. A twelve-year-old could read Harper Lee's *To Kill a Mockingbird*, a ninety-year-old Anne Tyler's *Breathing Lessons*, and be very happy.

There are no quotas for men, women or races in choosing these books. The only constraint on our choice was the lack of availability from certain countries. Otherwise we began and ended with open minds and the books we chose are here because we love them.

We both have memories from childhood and adolescence of being wrapped up in books. Books were a way of escaping the world, but also of entering it in a manner that was more intense; a way of discovering feeling, a working out of how to live.

Both of us were constantly reminded, as we did the research for this book, of moments from childhood and adolescence – finding a book we hadn't read, and after a few pages suddenly being enclosed, cocooned, absorbed and totally involved in the world of the book; finding ourselves anxious and dispossessed until we took the book up again and returned to its familiar world.

Books were happiness. We were brought up in places where reading was a passion and a joy. It still is for us. And so here they are: books that we offer wholeheartedly to the reader as you would give a guide to a friend going on a journey; 194 examples of the best novels and stories in English, published during the last half of the century.

The following are extracts from *The Modern Library*

Samuel Beckett 1906-1989

1955-1960 'The Molloy Trilogy'

Molloy 1955
Malone Dies 1958
The Unnamable 1960

Samuel Beckett's trilogy, published first in French in the early 1950s, and then translated by the author (with Patrick Bowles as a collaborator on *Molloy*) and published in English some years later, remains his monumental achievement in prose fiction, although some of his later short prose fiction is magnificent. He is concerned in his prose, and in his plays, to deal once and for all with the idea of narrative and character and plot. His characters think and remember, but this does not help them; they are sure that Being is a sour joke inflicted on them. They know they are alive because their bodies tell them so, and constantly humiliate them.

The drama is between action and inaction, between the possibility that the next sentence will lead us nowhere, or further back, or forward into a joke, or a snarl, or a nightmare, or a terrible darkness. Some of the writing – the sentence construction, the rhythms, the pacing and timing, the voice – is exquisitely beautiful, not a word out of place, but at the same time every word out of place, every word (and, indeed, every action and memory) open to constant interpretation, revaluation, negation. The tone in the last volume becomes more dense and difficult, and at times more simple and stark. 'This silence they are always talking about, from which supposedly he came, to which he will return when his act is over, he doesn't know what it is, nor what he is meant to do, in order to deserve it.' These are books to be read and reread.

Samuel Beckett was born in Ireland. He lived most of his life in France, where he died. He won the Nobel Prize for Literature in 1969.

Age in years these books were published: 49-54.

Barbara Vine (Ruth Rendell) 1930–

1986 A Dark-Adapted Eye

Ruth Rendell writes under two names, her own and that of Barbara Vine. The Rendell novels are, generally, detective novels centring on Chief Inspector Wexford and the fictional southern English town of Kings-markham, whilst those written under the name of Barbara Vine are psychological novels in the manner of Dickens or Wilkie Collins. To start on her detective novels, read *From Doon with Death* (1964), a Rendell classic. And so too is *A Dark-Adapted Eye*, her first Barbara Vine novel. Set in Suffolk, mostly in the 1950s, this story of the Longley women, Vera and Eden, uses the things that English gentlewomen do – embroidery, baking, keeping a spotless house, making do and behaving as women should – as a foil for what they also do in secrecy, in pursuit of power. This story of love and murder between sisters has such impact that the very trees in the Suffolk lanes arch up to warn of the damage wreaked, particularly on their menfolk, by women such as these, tightlaced in snobbery, fighting for life within rigid social rules.

There is more to this wily novel than meets the eye. The Longley clan always speak in 'half-shades and half-truths' and thus Barbara Vine ends this novel . . . the other half of the truth being there for us to find out if we can.

Ruth Rendell was born in London and lives in Suffolk. Many of her novels have won awards and have been televized. *A Dark-Adapted Eye* won the Mystery Writer of America Edgar Allan Poe Award.

Age in year of publication: 56.

The Modern Library *by Carmen Callil and Colm Tóibín will be published by Picador.*

from The Ballad of H.M.S. Belfast: A Compendium of Belfast Poems

by Ciaran Carson

Ciaran Carson's award-winning writing in both prose and poetry on his native city of Belfast provides us with an indispensable guidebook to a side of the city few will know exists. The poems here are a testament to his truly original voice.

Slate Street School

Back again. Day one. Fingers blue with cold. I joined
   the lengthening queue.
Roll-call. Then inside: chalk-dust and iced milk, the
   smell of watered ink.
Roods, perches, acres, ounces, pounds, tons weighed
   imponderably in the darkening
Air. We had chanted the twelve-times table for the
   twelfth or thirteenth time
When it began to snow. Chalky numerals shimmered
   down; we crowded to the window—

These are the countless souls of purgatory, whose numbers
   constantly diminish
And increase; each flake as it brushes to the ground is yet
   another soul released.
And I am the avenging Archangel, stooping over mills
   and factories and barracks.

48

I will bury the dark city of Belfast forever under snow:
inches, feet, yards, chains, miles.

Belfast Confetti

Suddenly as the riot squad moved in, it was raining
   exclamation marks,
Nuts, bolts, nails, car-keys. A fount of broken type. And
   the explosion
Itself – an asterisk on the map. This hyphenated line, a
   burst of rapid fire . . .
I was trying to complete a sentence in my head, but it
   kept stuttering,
All the alleyways and side-streets blocked with stops and
   colons.

I know this labyrinth so well – Balaclava, Raglan,
   Inkerman, Odessa Street—
Why can't I escape? Every move is punctuated. Crimea
   Street. Dead end again.
A Saracen, Kremlin-2 mesh. Makrolon face-shields.
   Walkie-talkies. What is
My name? Where am I coming from? Where am I
   going? A fusillade of question-marks.

The Ballad of H.M.S. Belfast: A Compendium of Belfast Poems
               by Ciaran Carson will be published by Picador.

from Honey-Dew

by Louise Doughty

Writer and broadcaster Louise Doughty's fascination with what appears to be ordinary in a twisted world has resulted in three highly acclaimed novels – Crazy Paving, Dance With Me and Honey-Dew. When a brutal murder punctures the tranquillity of a rural idyll, a local newspaper reporter endeavours to unravel the truth.

Miss Crabbe's favourite was *Have His Carcase*. She would often flick through it in search of inspiration. 'Carcase' was a wonderful word. A lesser writer would have used 'corpse' – but you could always rely on Dorothy to move beyond the expected phrase. That was why, in Miss Crabbe's opinion, she was streets ahead of boring old Agatha Christie. 'Agatha Crispy', Miss Crabbe called her – all that brisk prose.

The discovery of the body was the most important single event in a murder story – far more important than the murder itself, which usually happened off-stage and quite right too. She couldn't stand those modern novelists who went in for graphic garrotting and exploding eyeballs. How tasteless to describe all those horrible things happening to a living person.

A dead person was fair game. You could be as horrible as you liked to the dead – the more horrible the better. It

50

was important to establish from the outset that your victim was a thing, a conundrum.

> Harriet put the head down again and felt suddenly sick. She had written often enough about this kind of corpse, but meeting the thing in the flesh was quite different. She had not realised how butcherly the severed vessels would look, and she had not reckoned with the horrid halitus of blood, which steamed to her nostrils under the blazing sun. Her hands were red and wet. She looked down at her dress. That had escaped, thank goodness.

Miss Crabbe learned something every time she re-read *Have His Carcase*. It was vital, for instance, that your protagonist was shocked. It would be very bad form if they weren't.

'Butcherly' – what a wonderful adjective.

Much as she loved murder, Miss Crabbe had no feelings either way about violence. Real violence was to her – like having a child or eating peanut butter – quite unimaginable.

Like many things with the potential for inspiring fear, it had a tendency to inspire amusement. Occasionally, at the weekend, she would catch a repeat of *Bugs Bunny* or *Tom & Jerry* and would sit roaring at the television. It seemed entirely reasonable that if you hit somebody in the face with an iron, their features would flatten momentarily before springing back. She loved hospital dramas. The build-up to the calamity was best. Who could resist watching the old man cross the street, the schoolboy climb a tree, the mother drive with her toddler strapped safely into the back seat? Somehow, and soon, they would all coincide in the same casualty department. It was pure Sophocles.

Channel Four had recently started running a first-aid series, one of those ten-minutes-because-there's-a-gap-in-the-schedule programmes. Miss Crabbe tuned in religiously. It amazed her how stupid some people could be. Especially mothers. Mothers were the most stupid of all.

One episode was about how to deal with scalds and burns. A mother with a lot of Formica in her kitchen was cooking dinner; pie in the oven, vegetables on the hob. A silly little boy, eight years old or so, rushed into the kitchen and tipped a pan all over himself. Naturally, he began to scream and the mother dialled 999. At this point, a handsome-sounding man began a voiceover: 'Run cold water over him for fifteen minutes' etc. When the paramedics rushed in and asked what had happened, the panicking housewife shouted, 'He scalded himself! The carrots!'

Faced with melodrama such as this, Miss Crabbe had a tendency to become literal-minded. 'It wasn't the carrots,' she murmured at the screen, 'it was the hot water, *actually*.'

To her way of thinking, such mishaps were intimately connected to the intelligence of the recipient. Violence happened to people who, unlike her, did not have the common sense to avoid it.

On Sundays, she was fond of skimming through the colour supplement of her newspaper on the lookout for her favourite advertisement. It featured an elderly woman sprawled helplessly on the sitting room carpet, next to a beige sofa. A telephone sat on a coffee table, a tantalizing three feet away. The elderly woman could not reach it. Fortunately, she had a large red button strapped to her wrist. While her face looked sadly up at the distant phone, the finger of her other hand was pressing the button. The caption beneath the picture read, 'Mrs Hope knows help is coming. Would you?'

Week in, week out, the same advertisement appeared, although the picture varied. Sometimes, Mrs Hope would have tumbled down the stairs. Her arms would be splayed and she would appear to be in a coma but she must have managed to press the button before she sank into unconsciousness because she still knew help was coming. On other occasions, she had slipped in the bathroom. It seemed she had been trying to get out of (or into) the bath while wearing a fluffy dressing gown and full make-up.

Miss Crabbe found herself quite addicted to Mrs Hope's exploits and would leaf through the supplement each Sunday while other sections of the paper lay on the coffee table unread. 'Mrs Hope knows help is coming. Would you?' I have a question of my own, Miss Crabbe would think, reaching out a languid hand for her Sunday morning treat, a Bourbon biscuit, 'Why is Mrs Hope so accident-prone?'

Honey-Dew *by Louise Doughty will be published by Scribner.*

from Mapping the Edge
by Sarah Dunant

Sarah Dunant is the author of seven novels, most recently Transgressions. *She has won the Silver Dagger Award for crime fiction and has for many years been a cultural commentator on radio and television.*

People go missing every day. They walk out of their front doors and their lives into the silence of cold statistics. For those left behind it is the cruellest of the long goodbyes, because for them there is only pain and doubt. Did that person whom you loved so much – and thought you knew so well – did they simply choose to go and not come back? Or is it darker than that and did someone do the choosing for them?

Missing rubs the soul raw. In place of answers all you have is your imagination. In place of reality, only fantasy. And the more you think about it, the more elaborate and the more consuming those fantasies become.

Stories from the edge.

Like this one.

Anna is leaving home. Bye bye.

Mapping the Edge *by Sarah Dunant will be published by Little, Brown.*

from The Loop

by Nicholas Evans

Nicholas Evans is the author of the international bestseller
The Horse Whisperer. *From its breathtaking first chapter to its devastating climax,* The Loop *is an epic tale of a community riven by conflict and with a dangerous love affair at its heart.*

The scent of slaughter, some believe, can linger in a place for years. They say it lodges in the soil and is slowly sucked through coiling roots so that in time all that grows there, from the smallest lichen to the tallest tree, bears testimony.

Perhaps, as he moved silently down through the forest on that late afternoon, his summer-sleek back brushing lower limbs of pine and fir, the wolf sensed it. And perhaps this vestige of a rumor in his nostrils, that here a hundred years ago so many of his kind were killed, should have made him turn away.

Yet on and down he went.

He had set out the previous evening, leaving the others in the high country where even now, in July, there lingered spring flowers and patches of tired snow in gullies shy of the sun. He had headed north along a high ridge then turned east, following one of the winding rocky canyons that funneled the snowmelt down from the divide to the valleys and plains below. He had kept high, shunning the trails, especially those that ran along the water, where sometimes in this season there were humans. Even through the night, wherever it was possible, he had stayed below the timberline, edging the shadows, in a trot so effortless that his paws seemed to bounce without touching the ground. It was as though his journey had some special purpose.

When the sun rose, he stopped to drink, then found a shaded nook high among the sliprock and slept through the heat of the day.

Now, in this final descent to the valley, the going was more difficult. The forest floor was steep and tangled with blowdown, like tinder in some epic fireplace, and the wolf had to weave his way carefully among it. Sometimes he would double back and find a better route so as not to puncture the silence with the telltale snap of a dead branch. Here and there, the sun broke through the trees to make pools of vivid green foliage and these the wolf would always skirt.

He was a prime four-year-old, the alpha of the pack. He was long in the leg and almost a pure black, with just the faintest haze of gray along his flanks and at his throat and muzzle. Now and again he would pause and lower his head to sniff a bush or a tuft of grass, then lift his leg and make his mark, reclaiming this long-lost place as his own. At other times he would stop and tilt his nose to the air and his eyes would narrow and shine yellow as he read the scented messages that wafted on thermals from the valley below.

Once while doing this, he smelled something closer at hand and he turned his head and saw two white-tailed deer, mother and fawn, no more than a dozen yards away, frozen in a shaft of sunlight, watching him. He stared at them, connecting in an ancient communion that even the fawn understood. And for a long moment, all that moved were the spores and insects that spiraled and glinted above the deers' heads. Then, as if deer and insect were of equal consequence to a wolf, he looked away and again assessed the air.

From a mile and a half away came the mingled smells of the valley. Of cattle, dogs, the acrid tang of man's machines. And though he must have known, without ever being taught, the peril of such things, yet on again he went and down, the deer following him with inscrutable black eyes until he was lost among the trees.

The valley which the wolf was now entering ran some ten miles due east in a widening, glacial scoop toward the town of Hope. Its sides were ridged and thick with pine and, viewed from above, seemed to reach out like yearning arms to the great sunbleached plains that stretched from the town's eastern edge to the horizon and countless more beyond.

At its widest, from ridge to ridge, the valley was almost four miles wide. It was hardly perfect grazing land, though many had made a living from it and one or two grown rich. There was too much sage and too much rock and whenever the pasture seemed about to roll, some coulee or creek, choked with scrub and boulders, would gouge through and cut it off. Halfway down the valley, several of these creeks converged and formed the river which wound its way through stands of cottonwood to Hope and on from there to the Missouri.

All of this could be surveyed from where the wolf now stood. He was on a limestone crag that jutted from the trees like the prow of a fossilized ship. Below it, the land fell away sharply in a wedge-shaped scar of tumbled rock and, below that, both mountain and forest gave way grudgingly to pasture. A straggle of black cows and calves were grazing lazily at their shadows and beyond them, at the foot of the meadow, stood a small ranch house.

It had been built on elevated ground above the bend of a creek whose banks bristled with willow and chokecherry. There were barns to one side and white-fenced corrals. The house itself was of clapboard, freshly painted a deep oxblood. Along its southern side ran a porch that now, as the sun elbowed into the mountains, was bathed in a last throw of golden light. The windows along the porch had been opened wide and net curtains stirred in what passed for a breeze.

From somewhere inside floated the babble of a radio and maybe it was this that made it hard for whoever was at home to hear the crying of the baby. The dark blue buggy on the porch rocked a little and a pair of pink arms stretched craving for attention from its rim. But no one came. And at last, distracted by the play of sunlight on his hands and forearms, the baby gave up and began to coo instead.

The only one who heard was the wolf.

Kathy and Clyde Hicks had lived out here in the red house for nearly two years now and, if Kathy were honest with herself (which, on the whole, she preferred not to be, because mostly you couldn't do anything about it, so why give yourself a hard time?), she hated it.

Well, hate was maybe too big a word. The summers were OK. But even then, you always had the feeling that you were too far away from civilization; too exposed. The winters didn't bear thinking about.

They'd moved up here two years ago, right after they got married. Kathy had hoped having the baby might change how she felt about the place and in a way it had. At least she had someone to talk to when Clyde was out working the ranch, even though the conversation, as yet, was kind of one-way.

She was twenty-three and sometimes she wished she'd waited a few years to get married, instead of doing it straight out of college. She had a degree in agri-business management from Montana State in Bozeman and the only use she'd ever made of it was the three days a week she spent shuffling her daddy's paperwork around down at the main ranch house.

Kathy still thought of her parents' place as home and often got into trouble with Clyde for calling it that. It was only a couple of miles down the road, but whenever she'd spent the day there and got in the car to come back up here, she would feel something turn inside her that wasn't quite an ache, more a sort of dull regret. She would quickly push it aside by jabbering to the baby in the back or by finding some country music on the car radio, turning it up real loud and singing along.

She had her favorite station on now and as she stood at the sink shucking the corn and looking out at the dogs sleeping in the sun by the barns, she started to feel better. They were playing that number she liked, by the Canadian woman with the ball-breaker voice, telling her man how good it felt when he 'cranked her tractor'. It always made Kathy laugh.

God, really, she should count her blessings. Clyde was as fine a husband as any woman could hope for. Though not the richest (and, OK, maybe not the brightest either), he'd been, by a long way, the best-looking guy at college. When he'd proposed, on graduation day, Kathy's friends had been sick with envy. And now he'd given her a beautiful, healthy baby. And even if this place was at the back end of nowhere, it was still a place of their own. There were plenty of folk her age in Hope who'd give their right arms for it. Plus, she was tall, had great hair and even though she hadn't quite got her figure back after having the baby, she still knew her looks could crank any tractor she chose.

Self-esteem had never been a problem for Kathy. She was Buck Calder's daughter and around these parts that was about as big a thing to be as there was. Her daddy's ranch was one of the largest spreads this side of Helena and Kathy had grown up feeling like the local princess. One of the few things she didn't like about being married was giving up her name. She had even suggested to Clyde that she might do what those big-shot career women did nowadays and go double-barreled, call herself Kathy Calder Hicks. Clyde had said fine, whatever, but she could see he wasn't keen on the idea and so as not to hurt him she'd settled for plain old Kathy Hicks.

She looked up at the clock. It was getting on for six. Clyde and her daddy were down in the hay fields, fixing some irrigation, and they were all coming over for supper around seven. Her mom was due any minute with a pie she'd baked for dessert. Kathy cleared the mess out of the sink and put the corn into a pan on the stove. She wiped her hands on her apron and turned the radio down. All she had left to do was peel the potatoes and, when they were done, Buck Junior out there on the porch would no doubt be hollering for his feed and she'd do that then get him all bathed and brushed up nice and smart for his grandpa.

The cows in the top meadow looked up as one when the wolf came out from the trees. He stopped where the grass began, as if to give them the chance to inspect him. They had never before seen such a creature. Perhaps they placed him as some larger, darker kind of coyote. Coyotes were only a real danger when a calf was freshly born. Perhaps he seemed more like one of the ranch dogs who wandered among them sometimes and the only time you had to pay heed to them was when they snapped at your heels to make you go some place you'd rather not.

In return the wolf barely graced them with a glance. All his senses were locked on something else, something down at the house, and he lowered his head and started down the meadow toward it. He moved more slowly now, with greater caution, not skirting the cattle but passing right through them. But so clear was his disinterest that none moved away and all soon went back to their grazing.

As the sun slid behind the mountains, a line of shadow came creeping across the grass in front of the house and up and onto the porch, like a rising tide, so that first the wheels and then the base of the baby's buggy were engulfed and the oxblood wall behind it congealed to a darker red.

The wolf by now was at the foot of the meadow and here he stopped by the fence where Clyde had rigged up a pipe and an old enamel bathtub to water the cattle if the creek dried up. A pair of magpies broke from the willow scrub down by the creek and came up toward him in a series of fluttering swoops, scolding him, as if they knew his business here and didn't much care for it. The wolf ignored them. But from the shelter of his buggy, now only some twenty yards away, the baby did a passable imitation of the birds, shrieked with delight at how it sounded then did several encores. Inside the house a phone started to ring.

It was Kathy's mother. She said the pie had burned but not to worry because she had something else in the freezer that they could microwave.

'Oh and Luke says he'll come, if that's OK.'

'Of course it's OK.'

Luke, Kathy's brother, had just turned eighteen. He was sweet with the baby whenever she bumped into him down at the ranch, but he and Clyde didn't get along too well and since she'd been married, Luke hadn't been up here to the house more than a couple of times. As kids, they had never really been close. But then no one was close to Luke. Except, of course, their mom. She was the only one, in the end, who could handle his stutter.

Kathy had always been too impatient. Even when she was old enough to know better, she couldn't help finishing his sentences for him when he blocked. Since he'd graduated from high school, a couple of months ago, she'd hardly seen him. He was getting to be more of a loner than ever, it seemed to Kathy, always off on his own in the wilderness with only that funny-looking horse of his for company.

Anyway, he was coming to supper and that was fine.

Her mother asked how the baby was and Kathy said he was just great and that she'd better get off the phone because it was coming up toward his feed time and she still had things to do.

It was just as she hung up that the dogs started barking. Normally, she wouldn't have given this a second thought. The dogs were forever hollering and taking off after some varmint or other. But there was something about the noise they were making now that made her look out of the window.

Maddie, the old collie, had her tail tucked under her and was slinking off around the side of the barn, muttering over her shoulder. Prince, the yellow Labrador that Kathy's father had given her when they first moved up here, was pacing to and fro with his hackles up. His ears alternately pricked and flattened as if he were unsure of himself and he punctuated his barking with worried little whines. His eyes were fixed on something beyond the house, something up toward the meadow.

Kathy frowned. She'd better go see what was spooking them. The pan in which she was cooking the corn started to hiss and she went over to the stove and turned down the heat. When she came out through the kitchen screen door and stepped down into the yard, there was no sign of the collie. Prince seemed relieved to see her.

'Hey, you, what's going on here?'

The dog started to come toward her, then seemed to change his mind. Perhaps her presence gave him that little extra courage he'd been lacking, for now he took off in full cry around the side of the house, kicking up the dust as he went.

It was only then that the thought struck her. The baby. There was something on the porch, getting at the baby. She started to run. It must be a bear. Or a mountain lion. God, how could she have been so dumb?

As she came around the corner of the house, Kathy

saw, directly below the porch, what at first she took for a big, black dog, a German Shepherd maybe. It turned to face the Labrador's charge.

'Get out of here! Git!'

The animal glanced at her and she felt the yellow flash of his eyes upon her and knew in that instant this was no dog.

Prince had skidded to a halt before the wolf and had lowered himself, his front paws splayed so that his chest was just inches from the ground. He had his teeth bared and was snarling and barking but with such timid bravado that it seemed he might at any moment roll over and submit. The wolf stood very still, but somehow at the same time seemed to make himself bigger so that he towered over the dog. His tail was bushy and raised high. Slowly, he curled back his lips and snarled and his long incisors showed white.

Then, in a single lunge, he had his jaws on the Labrador's throat and swung him off his feet and through the air as if he were no heavier than a jackrabbit. The dog yelped and Kathy had a sudden image in her head of the wolf having already done the same with her baby and she screamed and jumped onto the end of the porch.

The buggy was at the far end and it seemed like a hundred miles away as she ran toward it.

Oh God, please. Don't let him be dead. Please don't let him be dead.

She couldn't tell whether the buggy had been disturbed, but even through the dog's shrieking, she knew her baby inside was silent and the thought of what she would find made her sob.

When she got there she hardly dared to look. But she forced herself and saw the child staring up at her, his face breaking into a gummy grin, and she cried out and reached down and snatched him up. She did it with such sudden violence that the child began to cry and she held him to her so hard that he cried even louder. She turned, pressing her back to the wall, and looked down from the porch.

The wolf was standing with his head lowered over the Labrador. Kathy could see right away that the dog was dead. His hind legs gave a final twitch, just like they did in his dreams when he slept in front of the fire. His throat had been torn out and his belly gaped like a gutted fish. The bleached grass under him rivered red. Kathy screamed again and the wolf started, as if he'd forgotten she was there. He stared right at her and she could see the glisten of blood on his face.

'Get out of here! Go on! Get out!'

She looked around for something to throw at him but there was no need. The wolf was already running off and within moments he was ducking under the fence and loping up among the cattle who had all quit their grazing to watch the spectacle below. At the top of the meadow he stopped and looked back to where Kathy still stood over the dead dog, clutching her baby and crying. Then he turned and vanished into the shadow of the forest.

The Loop *by Nicholas Evans will be published in Corgi Paperback.*

from Ex Libris: Confessions of a Common Reader

by Anne Fadiman

In Ex Libris, *award-winning journalist and editor Anne Fadiman wittily recounts her lifelong obsession with books and language. Perfect for all book-lovers,* Ex Libris *is a wonderful excursion into the world of literary gluttony.*

My Ancestral Castles

When I was four, I liked to build castles with my father's pocket-sized, twenty-two-volume set of Trollope. My brother and I had a set of wooden blocks as well, but the Trollopes were superior: midnight blue, proportioned to fit a child's hand, and, because they were so much thinner than they were tall, perfect, as cards are, for constructing gates and drawbridges. I own them now. Before I wrote these sentences, I took down three of the volumes from my shelves, and before you could say Sir Raffle Buffle, *The Last Chronicle of Barset* had become a lintel balanced precariously atop the twin posts of *Lady Anna* and *Doctor Thorne*.

I can think of few better ways to introduce a child to books than to let her stack them, upend them, rearrange them, and get her fingerprints all over them. It's a wonder to me that the young Diana Trilling, who had to wash her hands before she extracted a volume of Twain or Balzac from her parents' glass-fronted bookcase, grew up to be a booklover. Our parents' model was the playground; her parents' model was the operating room. By buying his set of leatherbound classics en bloc from a door-to-door salesman, Trilling's father committed the additional heresy, unimaginable to us, of believing that a library could be one-size-fits-all rather than bespoke. My brother and I were able to fantasize far more extravagantly about our parents' tastes and desires, their aspirations and their vices, by scanning their bookcases than by snooping in their closets. Their selves were on their shelves.

Our father's library spanned the globe and three millennia, although it was particularly strong in English poetry and fiction of the eighteenth and nineteenth centuries. The only junk, relatively speaking, was science fiction; the only wholly extraliterary works were about wine and cheese. My favorite shelf held the books he had written himself. I liked seeing my own name up there – FADIMAN FADIMAN FADIMAN – especially around the age of five, since it was one of the first words I learned to spell. When my reading skills improved, I remember imagining that Erasmus must have looked like Ed Wynn because he had written something called *In Praise of Folly*. My brother remembers thinking (more accurately) that Kierkegaard must have been a terrifying fellow because he had written *The Sickness unto Death* and *Fear and Trembling*. And we both believed that our father, because his books did, somehow managed to incorporate both folly and terror, as well as every emotion in between.

Our mother's library was narrower, focusing almost entirely on China and the Philippines. Paging through *A Primer in the Writing of Chinese Characters* (published in Shanghai!) and *I Was on Corregidor* (it mentioned *her*!) was thrilling, like discovering one was the illegitimate offspring of Mata Hari. But the excitement was not unalloyed. Our father, who often boasted that he had never actually done anything except think, was still the same person he had been when he started collecting books in the early 1920s. He and his library had never diverged. Our mother, on the other hand, had once led a life of action. And why had she stopped? *Because she had had children.* Her books, which seemed the property of a woman I had never met, defined the size of the sacrifice my brother and I had exacted.

Between them, our parents had about seven thousand books. Whenever we moved to a new house, a carpenter would build a quarter of a mile of shelves; whenever we left, the new owners would rip them out. Other people's walls looked naked to me. Ours weren't flat white backdrops for pictures. They were works of art themselves, floor-to-ceiling mosaics whose vividly pigmented tiles were all tall skinny rectangles, pleasant to the touch and even, if one liked the dusty fragrance of old paper, to the sniff. Vladimir Nabokov once recorded in his diary that at the age of eight, his son associated the letters of the alphabet with particular colors. *C* was yellow; *F* was tan; *M* was robin's-egg blue. To this day, imprinted by the cloth-covered spines of the books that surrounded me thirty years ago, I feel certain that Sophocles is terracotta, Proust is dove gray, Conrad is cinnamon, Wilde is acid green, Poe is Prussian blue, Auden is indigo, and Roald Dahl is mauve.

There must be writers whose parents owned no books, and who were taken under the wing of a neighbor or teacher or librarian, but I have never met one. My daughter is seven, and some of the other second-grade parents complain that their children don't read for pleasure. When I visit their homes, the children's rooms are crammed with expensive books, but the parents' rooms are empty. Those children do not see their parents reading, as I did every day of my childhood. By contrast, when I walk into an apartment with books on the shelves, books on the bedside tables, books on the floor, and books on the toilet tank, then I know what I would see if I opened the door that says PRIVATE – GROWNUPS KEEP

OUT: a child sprawled on the bed, reading.

My parents were merely passing on the legacy they had received from their own parents. When my mother moved from Utah to California at age nine, her father covered a sixteen-foot-long wall with bookcases, and her mother sheathed each shelf with nubbly beige wallpaper. My mother spent that summer reading the complete works of Dickens. My father grew up in Brooklyn in an immigrant family too poor to take him to a restaurant until he reached his teens, but not too poor to fill two black-walnut bookcases with the likes of Scott, Tolstoy, and Maupassant. 'I read Ibsen when I was eight,' he told me. 'Even before that, Ibsen was *there*. I knew he was a great Norwegian dramatist, part of a world I was somehow moving toward.' Last week he startled me by reciting, in an Irish accent, several lines spoken by Private Mulvaney in Kipling's *Soldiers Three*, which he had read (in a red edition with the title stamped in gold) eighty-five years earlier.

When I was fourteen, I noticed that the Late Augustan shelves in my father's British section contained a book that was turned spine in. Naturally, I made a beeline for it. It was *Fanny Hill*. (The effort to shield my innocent eyes was so obviously destined to backfire that a couple of years later, when I borrowed Freud's *Psychopathology of Everyday Life* from the Austrian shelf, I concluded my father had unconsciously *wanted* me to find *Fanny Hill*.) It is my opinion that parental bookcases are an excellent place for teenagers and erotica to meet for the first time, especially if the works are of high literary quality (John Cleland, Frank Harris, and Anaïs Nin, let us say, rather than Xaviera Hollander). Not only are the books easy to access, but the teenagers learn that, incredible as it may seem, their parents have sexual feelings too. *Fanny Hill* looked well thumbed.

When I asked several writers I know what books they remembered from their own parents' shelves, a high proportion were lubricious. Campbell Geeslin, a novelist and editor who grew up on a West Texas ranch, spent many hours in the embrace of *A Treasury of Art Masterpieces*, particularly the color reproduction of Manet's *Olympia*, whom he describes as 'wearing nothing but a black ribbon around her throat, with her legs slightly crossed to hide the part I most wanted to see'. The scholar and poet Charles Bell, whose father owned the second largest library in Mississippi, pored over the more risqué passages in Richard Burton's sixteen-volume translation of *The Thousand and One Nights*. When he inherited the set half a century ago, he discovered an oh-so-faintly penciled list of numbers on the back flyleaf of volume 4: page references to his dead father's own favorite salacities.

Those sixteen volumes now grace Charles Bell's library, one of the largest in Santa Fe. Campbell Geeslin did not inherit *A Treasury of Art Masterpieces*, only the fruitwood coffee table upon which it once reposed. He did, however, inherit the family Bible. Sixty years ago, his father read a chapter from it every night, leading Campbell to believe that Saul and David spoke with West Texas accents. During the readings, his mother sat at her dressing table, applying Pond's cold cream. 'Whenever I open the Bible today,' says Campbell, 'I hear my father's voice and I smell my mother's face.'

Some of my friends do not intend to leave their books to their children, believing that they would be a burden: a never-ending homework assignment, boxed and unboxed with every move, that would reproach the legatees from on high. I do not agree. I intend to leave my library to my children. My daughter already likes to look at our books and imagine what they might be about. (*Rabbit at Rest* is 'the story of a sleepy bunny'; *One Man's Meat* is 'a mystery about some men at a dinner table, and one of them gets steak but the others only get broccoli'.) Someday she will read them, as I read *In Praise of Folly*, whose Holbein frontispiece of Erasmus looked nothing like Ed

Wynn. My disappointment was part of growing up.

Seven years ago, when my parents moved from a large house to a small one, my brother and I divided the library overflow. My brother, who helped them pack, telephoned me from California, announcing each author as he emptied the bookcases. 'Chekhov?' he asked. 'Sure,' I replied. 'Turgenev?' 'Uh' – I was mentally gauging my shelf space – 'I guess not.' Later, of course, I kicked myself for having spurned Turgenev. The four hundred volumes that passed to me (which included the Trollopes but, unfortunately, not *Fanny Hill*) were at first segregated on their own wall, the bibliothecal equivalent of a separate in-law apartment.

'You just don't want your father's Hemingways to be sullied by my Stephen Kings,' said George accusingly.

'That's not true.'

He tried another tack. 'Your father wouldn't want his books to be a shrine. Didn't you say he used to let you build *castles* with them?'

This hit home. I realized that by keeping his library intact, I had hoped I might be able to keep my father, who was then eighty-six, intact as well. It was a strategy unlikely to succeed.

So his Trollopes are now ensconced in our Victorian section, cheek by jowl with our decaying college paperbacks. But I've been thinking of moving them to a lower shelf. Our two-year-old son is beginning to show an interest in building.

Ex Libris: Confessions of a Common Reader *by Anne Fadiman will be published in Allen Lane, The Penguin Press.*

from Sheer Blue Bliss

by Lesley Glaister

*Lesley Glaister was born in Wellingborough in 1956. She
teaches a Masters Degree in Writing at Sheffield Hallam
University. She is the author of* The Private Parts of
Women *and most recently* Easy Peasy.

**The effect of the elixir entering the bloodstream is
swift. The sensation is of lifting and lightening.
Ordinary objects may appear luminous with significance. Haloes are common.**

Tony closes his eyes and squeezes, trying to imagine
how it would be. Sees a sprinkle of bursting lights or a
spray like thin petals. Opens his eyes. No significance in
the ordinary objects here, not a halo in sight, though he
can see a glow of sun on dusty leaves outside the
window . . . But the elixirs, the elixirs would be something different. If they exist he will have them. That is his
reason and his purpose.

He grins at himself in a window, cool customer with
his long black hair, white shirt softened by the sun
and his body heat but still a stunning white . . . Girls
look at him as he walks, girls and boys. He exaggerates
the swing of his skinny hips. Thirty, could pass
for twenty-one easy, could fuck practically anyone on
this street if he felt so inclined, anyone would. So
magnetic, so charismatic. He has that special indefinable

something that nobody can deny.

Must get to that exhibition and see that portrait. Constance Benson, the lover. Must get to her. This is it, what he has been waiting for. With the scrap of paper in his hand he knows, it's like the right key fitting a lock. You have to be aware, alert. And Tony is. She'll recognize him all right. Recognize that Patrick has guided him to her, that he is the one she can trust with the elixirs, the one Patrick meant them for.

And then? But there is no need to think about and then. Because it will be plain after that. Plain sailing.

Sheer Blue Bliss *by Lesley Glaister was published by Bloomsbury.*

from Fish

by Sophie Grigson and William Black

Sophie Grigson – cook, columnist and television presenter – collected over 180 fabulous recipes for Fish, *in which William Black – a leading expert in matters piscine – discusses fish, fishing methods and fish ecology. In this recipe, tarragon adds life to a parcel of sea trout, wrapped in a jacket of filo pastry.*

Sea Trout in Filo Pastry with Tarragon

Alternative: salmon
French tarragon, with its sweet, green, aniseed flavour, is usually saved for chicken dishes but why should it be so restricted? It works admirably with fish, as long as it is not used with a heavy hand. Here it brings life to a pretty parcel of pink sea trout, wrapped in a crisp jacket of filo pastry.

SERVES 4

500g (1 lb 2 oz) skinned sea
   trout fillet, divided into
   4 portions
4 large sheets of filo pastry
30g (1 oz) butter, melted
salt and pepper

For the Tarragon Butter:
30g (1 oz) lightly salted or
   unsalted butter, softened
1 tablespoon chopped fresh
   tarragon leaves
finely grated zest of ½ lemon
2 teaspoons lemon juice
salt and pepper

Preheat the oven to 230°C/450°F/Gas Mark 8. Season the sea trout with salt and pepper. To make the tarragon butter, beat the butter with all the remaining ingredients, seasoning lightly if needed.

Extract the sheets of filo pastry from their packet. To prevent them from drying out, lay them on a table, cover with a sheet of greaseproof paper, then cover that with a tea towel wrung out in cold water.

Take the first sheet of filo, brush with melted butter and lay a piece of sea trout in the centre. Spread a quarter of the tarragon butter over it. Wrap the sea trout up neatly in the filo, keeping the tarragon-butter side on top but tucking the joins and ends away underneath. Lay on a greased baking sheet. Repeat with the remaining filo, sea trout and tarragon butter. Brush the tops and sides of the parcels with any remaining melted butter. Cover and keep cool for a short while if not cooking straightaway.

Bake the parcels, uncovered, for 5 minutes, then reduce the heat to 190°C/375°F/Gas Mark 5 and cook for a further 10-12 minutes. Serve immediately.

Fish *by Sophie Grigson and William Black was published by Headline.*

Round Ireland with a Fridge – Again

by Tony Hawks

Tony Hawks, comedian and author of the bestselling
Round Ireland with a Fridge, *relates the unusual tale*
behind a unique publishing phenomenon – the first time a
beer commercial has ever been based on the storyline of a
book.

In May 1997 I did something silly. Big-time silly. To win a
hundred-pound bet, which I had made when drunk, I
hitchhiked round the circumference of Ireland . . . *with a*
fridge. Yes, a fridge. A squat little drinks fridge which my
Irish hosts came to view as a personality in its own right.
It was christened 'Saiorse' (Gaelic for 'freedom'), was
cheered as I wheeled it into pubs on its trolley, and was
generally treated with the kind of respect not normally
granted to household appliances. One day someone had
the bright idea of signing their name across its door, and
it wasn't long before the entire fridge was covered in
autographs and goodwill messages. By the end of my trip
it had ceased to be a fridge but a work of art, no longer an
inanimate object but a trusty friend. So, it came as quite a
shock when I had to get used to allowing a new fridge into
my life.

The occasion came eighteen months later when, much
to my surprise, a lager company declared that they wanted
me to appear in a series of commercials based on my now

famous fridge journey. This was pleasant news, but I was disappointed to learn that it was felt that a larger fridge was going to be necessary.

'How do you feel about that?' they asked.

'Weird,' came my reply.

How could I go off with another fridge and be disloyal to Saiorse? And how could I let them know this was how I felt without them thinking I had completely lost my mind?

I hesitated and then said begrudgingly, 'I suppose I could get used to the idea.'

A month later I was in County Kerry with an entirely new fridge in my life. It seemed huge and it looked cold and unfriendly. I know that fridges are supposed to look cold but not when they're your travelling companion. I was shocked by the pristine whiteness and disappointed by its lack of manoeuvrability. In fact the only thing I really liked about it was its curvy handles.

Filming started, and the first shot involved me struggling up a steep hill pulling the fridge on its trolley. How different it was to my first experience. After each take, sturdy men jumped out from behind a bush and hauled the fridge back to its first position. Someone holding a walkie-talkie asked me if everything was OK or if I needed a cup a' tea. The pretty make-up girl would come and brush my hair one way or another and put some powder on my face. When I had some difficulty pushing the fridge over a stony path beneath it, a further sturdy man called Jimmy was supplied to get down on his hands and knees and help push the fridge up the hill. Twenty or so people looked on during each shot, each with their own allotted responsibility. It seemed astonishing to me that so many bodies were required. Director, assistant director, two producers, focus puller, make-up, hairdresser, two art directors, the copywriter, cameraman, sound technician, someone to check for continuity, clapper loader, grip, camera car driver, a dozen lighting electricians and miscellaneous crew, wardrobe supervisor, the clients . . . and me. Little old me, the 'eejit' who hitchhiked round Ireland with a fridge to win a hundred-pound bet.

The camera rolled, the sun shone and my heart swelled with pride. To my knowledge, this was the first time that an advertisement campaign had ever been based on a book. If I'd never taken on the original bet then none of this would have happened. Surely there had to be some kind of lesson to be learned here; after all, look how I had been rewarded for doing something which everyone had originally considered to be very silly. For some reason which I still cannot fathom, I had never viewed it that way and neither did the Irish. I had had their approval from the outset and shall always be grateful to them for that.

'Bejaysus, why are you bringing a feckin' fridge round with you?' I had regularly been asked.

'Because I'm trying to win a bet.'

'How much is the bet?'

'One hundred pounds.'

'And how much was the fridge?'

'One hundred and forty pounds.'

'Jeez, you're an eejit. What are you drinking?'

Pints and pints of Irish hospitality followed.

That's what I like about Ireland. I am convinced that there is no other place in the world where an act such as hitchhiking with a fridge could win universal approval, where people would say 'Fair play to you!' or 'Good idea!'

Perhaps Ireland's history, which had kept it on the fringes of European society for so long, had meant the Irish had developed a different perspective on these matters. They were mature enough to be child-like.

In the breaks between shooting I had conversations with locals and the memories of my original adventure came flooding back. Over a cup of tea I spent an agreeable ten minutes with Pat, the local policeman who had been assigned to look after us.

'Is there much crime in Kerry?' I asked him.

'No. Not really,' he replied.

'Don't you get people coming in from outside and causing trouble?'

'Not really, because of the shape of the Kerry peninsula. They'd have to leave the same way as they came in and we'd catch them on the road out, so they don't bother.'

'There must be people who are drunk and disorderly?'

'Oh, there's a bit of that, but I don't get involved.'

It was difficult to work out what he *did* do other than drink tea and chat. It was rather nice to think that was all that was required of him. Maybe the definition of a civilized society is a place where the policemen are only required to drink tea and chat.

Meanwhile there had been a crisis back 'on set'. The question had been raised as to whether the fridge had the right kind of handles. Art directors, producers, directors and the clients were involved in heated debate as to what message the present handles were communicating to the public at large.

'Do those handles really say domestic fridge?'

'Does it matter as long as you can see it's a fridge?'

'I just think a less curved and more angular handle conveys domesticity that much better.'

Of course, we all knew that.

'Well, if we change the handles, we'll have to do the first shot again.'

'Do you mind? I really think it's worth it.'

'No, if it makes you happier, then we'll re-shoot.'

'Thanks.'

And so poor Jimmy had to get back down on his hands and knees and shove the fridge all the way up the hill again. No one had the heart to tell him why.

It wasn't until the second day that we took the first shot of me hitching by the roadside. The scene seemed more surreal than ever with trucks, Land Rovers and catering vans strewn around the surrounding countryside. I stood patiently beside my fridge as I had done for so many hours on my initial journey, but this time I was waiting for a director to shout action before I stuck my thumb out. As the cars came past I saw that look on the drivers' faces which I had seen so many times before: 'Was that guy hitching with a *fridge*?'

However this time round, if anything the faces showed even more bewilderment: 'Was that guy hitching with a fridge *and* with an entire film crew recording the event?'

During one rehearsal a car pulled up beside me and the woman in the passenger seat got out and stood up to me.

'I don't believe it, I'm reading your bloody book at the moment!' she declared.

The lady proceeded to fish my book out of her bag and get me to sign it, and when she returned to her car the crew gave her a spontaneous round of applause. As she drove away she must have wondered whether fridge hitchhiking was all I *ever* did.

At the end of the four days two commercials had been shot. Everyone had enjoyed themselves and been paid handsomely for it. I had grown fond of my new fridge but it would never replace Saoirse, sitting patiently at home in my front room awaiting my return. 'Long may the spirit of Saoirse continue to spread wealth and joy,' I thought to myself.

We bade farewells to our hosts from Kerry who had made us so welcome and we drove off to the airport. I turned round for one more glimpse of this idyllic little setting and saw Pat the policeman waving goodbye in a most unpoliceman-like way. He seemed to epitomize the spirit of Ireland which meant most to me. Everyone knew that Pat wasn't really capable of preventing or solving any crime so nobody really bothered to commit any. It wouldn't have been right. It was a fragile state of affairs but for now it worked. A social system built on the absence of cynicism. As I saw Pat waving enthusiastically, for a moment I felt concerned for him and I turned to Paul the copywriter.

'Now that we're gone, what's he going to do?' I asked.

'Oh, he'll be all right,' replied Paul. 'There'll be enough tea and chatting to see him through.'

'You're right. More than enough. By the way, I forgot to ask, but what's going to happen to the fridge?'

'We're giving it to a children's charity.'

'Excellent. I'm glad it's gone to a good home.'

I hope they like the handles.

Tony Hawks's book Round Ireland with a Fridge *was published by Ebury Press.*

The Proposition

by Elizabeth Jane Howard

*Elizabeth Jane Howard is best known for her eleven
novels, published across five decades and including the
recent bestselling* Cazalet Chronicles. *She also wrote a
short story collection,* Mr Wrong, *from which* The
Proposition *is taken.*

Robin Boston-Crabbe had scarcely brought the Mercedes
to a halt before the commissionaire had a white-gloved
hand on the door handle of the car.

'Good morning, sir.'

'Morning. All right if I leave her here?'

The commissionaire clearly hesitated.

'I have an appointment to see Mr Medusa.'

The commissionaire's face cleared. 'Certainly, sir. You
know your way, sir?'

'No, but I imagine it's at the top.'

'Right, sir. But it's not on the board. I'll ring through
for you, sir.'

While he was doing this, Robin read the gold-painted
names of the other occupants of Dorado House, as the
luxury block was called. He also noticed that there were
two lifts, that nobody got into or came out of either of
them, that there were live goldfish in the pool round which
a number of opulent ferns were grouped, and that there
was no sign of a staircase or even of a door that led to one.

'Sorry to keep you waiting, sir.'

Robin had already moved towards the lifts, but as he was about to press a button to summon one, the mirrored panel between them swung gently open.

'Mr Medusa has his own lift.'

'So I see. Thank you.'

The walls were covered in cork flecked with gold and there were only two buttons. One said 'up' and the other 'down'. Robin pressed the 'up'.

In the lift he had time to feel nervous. This was the opportunity that so many waited all their lives for in vain: if he made the wrong impression now, he would never get another chance. He had dressed with care and he wore clothes well – had several times been asked, in fact, to model for some high-class advertisements that involved standing about in blazer or tweeds outside a country house leaning on a sports car or being leaned on by a red setter but, naturally, he had refused. He had always been careful of his image and, judging by this morning, it seemed to have paid off.

The butler was waiting for him; of course.

'Good morning, sir. Mr Medusa is expecting you.' He opened a red leather door and led the way down a passage lined two deep with Paul Klees. A further red leather door led into a very large sitting-room, studded with pots of flowering shrubs. A huge fireplace contained a log fire – burning now with some aromatic fragrance.

'If you will be seated, sir, I will inform Mr Medusa of your arrival.'

But Robin was too fascinated by the room to sit down in it. Apart from the pictures – Chagall, Soutine, de Staël, and others he did not recognize – there was a beautiful T'ang horse, and a silk rug in apricot and yellow. There was also an enormous pedimented mirror (Chippendale?) with amazingly carved cupids and fruit. He advanced upon this to have a final check-up of his appearance. His hair had really been very well cut; he smoothed it back

82

and gave himself a tentative, encouraging smile.

At that moment, a low, voluptuous growling began – like prickly velvet, and Robin turned sharply on his heel to find his host a few yards away and accompanied by the largest Alsatian he had ever seen.

'Mr Robin Boston-Crabbe! Be *quiet*, Felicity! I cannot say she is perfectly harmless – she is not. But she will do as I tell her.' He advanced to the fireplace and pulled a green silk tassel. Then he stood, a small, frail figure, wearing a superb tussore silk suit, with his back to the fire, surveying his guest in so penetrating a manner that Robin's general nerves accentuated to a specific shyness. The Alsatian subsided watchfully on the hearthrug and the butler reappeared.

'Ah, Ipswich. Champagne, please. If that suits you?'

'It sounds great.'

'Do sit down. You look in wonderful shape. Skiing evidently agrees with you.'

Robin smiled. He always knew exactly what shape he was in, but he liked to have it noticed.

'As a matter of fact, a film producer in Gstaad actually asked me whether I would be interested in appearing in a film he was doing.'

'Really? And what kind of film had he in mind?'

'Oh – one of those dear old super-spy epics.'

'How amusing! How extremely funny!' Mr Medusa's heavily hooded, almost turquoise eyes screwed up while he laughed. He was, Robin decided, not only a very striking man, but possessed of exceptional charm. It was impossible to determine his age.

He realized that Mr Medusa was again regarding him closely, and said, 'I was admiring your wonderful plants.'

'Were you really? Well, they *are* a joy. It is so teasing of camellias not to smell, but I've managed to get my chap to bring on the stephanotis to be with them. The best of both worlds, which is really the only point of having a little money. Give us a glass each and put the bucket next to Mr Boston-Crabbe, Ipswich.'

'I suppose it is.'

'Oh – come – you don't do too badly. That watch you are wearing would not lead one to imagine you are confined to supposition. Or perhaps it was – given to you?'

Robin could not help glancing at his Patek Philippe. 'As a matter of fact I bought it.'

Mr Medusa brought the palms of his hands together with a small papery thud. 'There you are! It is my opinion that you are quite rich enough for your age . . . One could not wish you to become – spoiled – in any way. But I admire your watch. I really do.' He raised his glass – the champagne was very nearly the colour of his hair. 'And what shall we drink to?'

Robin felt himself almost blushing. He must not seem unenthusiastic; he must not presume – he did not know what to say.

'Perhaps we should drink to the memory of poor Le Mesurier.'

Robin bowed his head and they both drank. Ipswich had left the room.

'You were with that gentleman for some years, I believe?'

'Nearly five.'

'Ah yes. And I have been told from – several sources – that he always found you most – satisfactory.'

Robin nodded, and kept his expression grave but reliable.

'Well! We won't rush things. What were you enjoying most about this room when I came into it? Apart from your own charming image, that is?'

Now he felt he *was* blushing. He mumbled something about the plants.

'You mustn't mind me. I'm a terrible tease. And you *do* look perfectly charming. Yes, I always have flowers growing as a matter of principle. Do you realize that all cut flowers are simply dying before one's eyes? And not only dying, probably dying a most slow and disagreeable death. A disgusting thought. I have never understood how people can stomach it. Death, when it has to come, should be instantaneous, don't you think? But of course you do. Could I trouble you for a little more champagne?'

When Robin bent to pour from the bottle he noticed that Mr Medusa's lightly tanned face was completely smooth – not a wrinkle or a fold of flesh to be seen.

'A good, steady hand,' Mr Medusa remarked approvingly. 'But then, one would expect that. I have one question to ask you – of a somewhat delicate nature. Oh – do help yourself.'

Robin did so, and then sat on the edge of his chair opposite his host.

'When you were with poor Le Mesurier, I take it you were – exclusively – with him? I have no wish to pry into any arrangements there may have been between you beyond this one point.'

Here it was: the one question that he had dreaded – that in all his private rehearsals of this interview he had been unable to decide how he should answer. Tell the truth, and he would be out on his ear; lie, and in all probability he would be detected and out on the other ear. To his surprise, Mr Medusa was not looking at him, was merely gazing intently at his champagne. He took the plunge.

'I did once go off – but the whole thing was only a weekend – it was before I realized Mr Le Mesurier's feelings in the matter, and after that I never did so again.'

There was a short silence, and Robin, already regretting his choice, added rather desperately: 'It was only once, and that's the truth.'

Then Mr Medusa did look at him. 'I know. I was afraid you might lie and I never look at people when I feel they may do that.' He drained his glass and held it out for more. 'I think we shall get along very nicely. You will have plenty of time to get used to my ways. I shall not want you to kill anybody for at least a month.'

Robin let out his breath.

'Thank you very much, Mr Medusa.'

The anthology Mr Wrong *by Elizabeth Jane Howard was published by Macmillan.*

from Birthday Letters
by Ted Hughes

Ted Hughes was born in Yorkshire in 1930. He published many volumes of poetry and prose, most recently Birthday Letters, *which transfigured his personal life into contemporary myth and confirmed his reputation as one of our truly great poets. He died in October 1998.*

Epiphany

London. The grimy lilac softness
Of an April evening. Me
Walking over Chalk Farm Bridge
On my way to the tube station.
A new father – slightly light-headed
With the lack of sleep and the novelty.
Next, this young fellow coming towards me.

I glanced at him for the first time as I passed him
Because I noticed (I couldn't believe it)
What I'd been ignoring.

Not the bulge of a small animal
Buttoned into the top of his jacket
The way colliers used to wear their whippets—
But its actual face. Eyes reaching out
Trying to catch my eyes – so familiar!

The huge ears, the pinched, urchin expression—
The wild confronting stare, pushed through fear,
Between the jacket lapels.

                              'It's a fox-cub!'
I heard my own surprise as I stopped.
He stopped. 'Where did you get it? What
Are you going to do with it?'

                              A fox-cub
On the hump of Chalk Farm Bridge!

'You can have him for a pound.' 'But
Where did you find it? What will you do with it?'
'Oh, somebody'll buy him. Cheap enough
At a pound.' And a grin.

                              What I was thinking
Was – what would you think? How would we fit it
Into our crate of space? With the baby?
What would you make of its old smell
And its mannerless energy?
And as it grew up and began to enjoy itself
What would we do with an unpredictable,
Powerful, bounding fox?
The long-mouthed, flashing temperament?
That necessary nightly twenty miles
And that vast hunger for everything beyond us?
How would we cope with its cosmic derangements
Whenever we moved?

The little fox peered past me at other folks,
At this one and at that one, then at me.
Good luck was all it needed.
Already past the kittenish
But the eyes still small,
Round, orphaned-looking, woebegone
As if with weeping. Bereft
Of the blue milk, the toys of feather and fur,
The den life's happy dark. And the huge whisper

Of the constellations
Out of which Mother had always returned.
My thoughts felt like big, ignorant hounds
Circling and sniffing around him.
                                   Then I walked on
As if out of my own life.
I let that fox-cub go. I tossed it back
Into the future
Of a fox-cub in London and I hurried
Straight on and dived as if escaping
Into the Underground. If I had paid,
If I had paid that pound and turned back
To you, with that armful of fox—

If I had grasped that whatever comes with a fox
Is what tests a marriage and proves it a marriage—
I would not have failed the test. Would you have failed it?
But I failed. Our marriage had failed.

Birthday Letters *by Ted Hughes was published*
by Faber & Faber.

from The Year 1000

by Robert Lacey and Danny Danziger

The Year 1000 *is a vivid and surprising portrait of life in England a thousand years ago – no spinach, no sugar but a world which already knew brain surgeons and property developers, and yes, even the occasional gossip columnist.*

The English Spirit

'And then there is also a need that each should understand where he came from and what he is – and what will become of him.'

Wulfstan, Archbishop of York from 1002 to 1023

A green and pleasant England with ample space to breathe, the sound of birdsong and church bells, the sharp smell of drifting woodsmoke on an autumn evening – life in the year 1000 can be evoked with some powerfully attractive images, and they are complemented by the mesmerically beautiful treasures that have been recovered from Anglo-Saxon churches and archaeological sites: two delicately entwined ivory angels from Winchester, twisting and fluttering heavenwards like the double propeller of a sycamore seed; a walrus tusk, now in Liverpool Museum, that must have been carved sometime very close to 1000 AD with two cheeky sheep peering out from below the manger of the Christ child; and from the tomb of the great Archbishop Wulfstan, who died in 1023 AD, an exquisitely slender bronze cloak pin – the very pin, presumably, with which he fastened his vestments before mounting to the pulpit – with a minuscule latticework of tracery etched on to its diamond-shaped head. The crafts-manship could not be bettered today.

But then in a grave at Kingsworthy in Hampshire are found the bones of a mother with the skeleton of her baby still inside her, trapped on its way along her birth canal. The woman must have died in the throes of labour without relief of medicine – let alone the drastic release offered by Caesar-ian section, which is not recorded as being attempted in England until the sixteenth century, with no mother reported as surviving the procedure until the eighteenth. Reconstruction of the Kingsworthy mother's pelvis shows it to have been narrow and constricted, while the bones of the infant are larger than average, suggesting a birthweight of nine to ten pounds. So the best explanation of these remains – as for those of another tragic skeleton found in London with foetal bones inside the abdomen – is that the mother died, almost certainly of sheer exhaustion, after long hours of trying vainly to deliver a child that never had a chance of being born. Death, disease and discomfort were daily com-panions in the year 1000, and living through the annual round of toil set out in the pages of the Julius Work Calendar represented a veritable triumph of the human spirit.

The simplest things were so difficult to accomplish. It took enormous time and effort to manufacture just one single coin, or to turn on a hand lathe the wooden cups that would today be produced in vast quantities by a machine. Every basic artefact represented hours of skill and effort and ingenuity, in return for a very meagre material reward. Kings and eminent churchmen lived in relative comfort, but there were no large or exaggerated profit margins for anyone. For the vast majority of ordi-nary people life was a struggle in even the smallest respect. Imagine wearing scratchy underwear made of coarse, hand-woven wool, since there was no cotton. Only the wealthy could afford garments of linen – and that was woven to a texture that would be too itchy for many a modern skin. The poetry of the year 1000 celebrated the qualities of the hero, and just to survive on a day-to-day basis, every man and woman had to be precisely that.

The most obvious difference between the year M and the year MM is the billions of extra people for whom this second millennium will possess some significance. Today the Jewish, Buddhist, and Moslem systems of datings still hold sway in their own cultures, where 2000 AD is numbered as 5760, 2544 and 1420 respectively. But the concept of the year 2000 and a new millennium has come to hold meaning for the world's many non-Christian societies, if only because of the computer systems which have turned out to be tied more intimately than intended to the system of dating popularized thirteen centuries ago by the Venerable Bede. For reasons grand, petty and sometimes just coincidental, the culture that was developing in the misty, north-west corner of Europe around the year 1000 has spread its values all over the modern world – and the drawings and Latin verses of the Julius Work Calendar provide some clues as to how and why this has happened.

The Calendar is dedicated to work and prayer. Its message is that you must labour as unquestioningly as you worship your God, and, as put into practice through the best part of the millennium that followed, this fundamental work ethic was to prove the basis of material success in England and in every other society that adopted it. Already in these drawings are intimations of what was to come in the industrial west. The January ploughman is handling his massive, stall-fed oxen like so many machines. They are animals, but he is using them as enormous engines that could accomplish so much more work in so much less time than could be achieved by unassisted human labour. It was this sort of mechanical energy which produced the food surplus which, over the centuries, was to support the ever-increasing proportion of English people living in towns – and it was through the towns that mass prosperity, and mass political freedom, was eventually won.

Looking at Europe in the year 1000, there were many societies for which one might have predicted wealth and empire ahead of England – and potentially at England's expense. The ambitious Ottoman emperors controlled the old capitals of both Charlemagne and the Roman empire. In Constantinople, the rulers of Byzantium maintained the tradition of that city's imperial greatness, while down in Spain, the Saracens threatened further conquests in the direction of the Christian kingdoms to the north. And then there were the empires based in Baghdad, Persia and India – and further east in Korea, China and Japan.

But all these locally dominant power structures were autocracies, and autocracy, in the long run, was not to prove the way ahead. It was inflexible and hidebound, fatally resistant to the spirit of innovation on which progress depends. The English may have looked foolish when they paid their Danegeld to the barbarous Vikings in the years around 1000, but at least they knew how to generate their money through enterprise rather than through crude conquest, and the taxes that were doubt-less raised with great grumbling could only have been levied and paid over so repeatedly on some ultimate basis of popular consent.

Consent and social co-operation are among the most difficult elements to define in any society, but they were to prove crucial for the long-term future of the English way. Sharing the technology of the plough-team was an exercise in communal organization. Archbishop Wulfstan's description of how an agricultural estate should be run in the year 1000 depended on slave labour and was built around the authority of a lord of the manor, but that authority could only operate by respecting the rights of the community. The English described themselves as 'subjects' in the year 1000, as they do today, but ten centuries of political development were to earn them rights and privileges that made them the envy of 'citizens' elsewhere.

Less attractively, the English were also about to embark on a long phase in their history in which they paid signally little respect to the rights of others. Within a hundred years they were to embark on their programme of global expansion that began with the Crusades – Christendom's gleefully-seized opportunity to hand back to the infidels a solid taste of the aggression from which Europe had already suffered – and England happily joined in that attack. She could thank the Normans for her warhorses, for her stone castles, and for a sharp new cutting edge to her military technology, but she financed all this with wealth that came from the wellsprings of the old Anglo-Saxon economy. Archaeology tells us of the coinage that both expressed and made possible the growing potency of English commerce, and this was to be enhanced by contemporary improvements in maths. The first Arabic numerals made their earliest appearance in a western document in 976 AD, and though centuries were to elapse before these numerals came into common commercial use, they pointed the way to the numeracy on which modern science, technology, business, and economics are all based.

The handful of wills and charters that have come down to us from Anglo-Saxon England reveal another ingredient of that society's future. The mundane precision with which these documents describe every detail of a particular estate boundary shows the seriousness with which the possession of property was taken in the year 1000, and though this was by no means unique to England, it was to prove another ingredient in the country's future success. In the eighteenth century Edmund Burke would argue that the sanctity of property was the basic prerequisite of economic enterprise, since incentive can have no meaning until society makes it possible for property to be held securely.

The ultimate guarantee of this security was a respect for the law, the fundamental engine of healthy social growth – the idea that no man can be above the law, least of all lords and kings as they exercise their power. This was already inherent in the law-codes regulating English life in the year 1000, and it helped provide this industrious society with an extraordinarily well developed sense of national identity. The concept of the nation state had yet to be articulated, and that concept was to engender much bloodshed and suffering, but it provided the lodestone of English existence for the next thousand years.

As we today look forward to a millennium in which supranational, global organization appears a very obvious key to the future, some may regard nationality as an outmoded concept. But nationality was the engine of England's progress in the centuries that followed the year 1000. Archbishop Wulfstan's mesmeric sermon to his fellow countrymen was both a doom-laden lament, and a clarion call to England's sense of itself. Geography was one vital factor, and language provided another, for though English democracy, technology and economic enterprise were to secure many conquests in the course of the next thousand years, it was the strength and flexibility of the English language which secured the most universal conquests of all.

The earliest documents that were written in *Englisc* tended by their nature towards formality if they were legal documents, and to conventional heroics if they were poems. But one Old English poem does survive that conveys something of the inner questioning, along with the stoic spirit of destiny, that inspired men and women to keep on battling with the realities of life at the turn of the first millennium:

Often and again, through God's grace,
Man and woman usher a child
Into the world and clothe him in gay colours;
They cherish him, teach him as the seasons turn
Until his young bones strengthen,
His limbs lengthen . . .

Entitled 'The Fortunes of Men', the poem was a medita-
tion on fate – *wyrd* in *Englisc*, literally 'what will be' – for
having described the fresh and innocent joy of a young
mother and father raising their children, the anonymous
author went on to examine the different destinies that a
first-millennial child might actually encounter in the
course of its life:

Hunger will devour one, storm dismast another,
One will be spear-slain, one hacked down in battle . . .

'The Fortunes of Men' offered a comprehensive catalogue of the hazards that a young man – or his worrying
parents – might fear in England in the year 1000, from
falling out of a tree at apple harvest time to a quarrel at a
feast where the drink flowed too free:

One will drop, wingless, from the high tree . . .
One will swing from the tall gallows . . .
The sword's edge will shear the life of one
At the mead-bench, some angry sot
Soaked with wine. His words were too hasty . . .

But life could offer joy and achievement as well – 'a young
man's ecstasy', suggested the poet, '. . . strength in wrest-
ling . . . skill in throwing and shooting . . . good fortune at
dice . . . a devious mind for chess'. Surveying the up-side,
'The Fortunes of Men' set out the earthly pleasures of
which people dreamed at the turn of the first millennium,
though the nature of the pleasures that the poet envisaged

for those favoured by Fate and God suggested the workings of a distinctly male ambition. The poet's wish list of sport, easy money, and a good time in the pub was that of any red-blooded twentieth-century lad:

> One will delight a gathering, gladden
> Men sitting at the mead-bench over their beer . . .
> One will settle beside his harp
> At his lord's feet, be handed treasures . . .
> One will tame that arrogant wild bird,
> The hawk on the fist, until the falcon
> Becomes gentle; he puts jesses on it . . .

The poet left his audience with the big question: which way will your life turn, to happiness or to some living tragedy? And *wyrd*, the answer in the year 1000, was as imponderably challenging as 'what will be' today. Only God, or Fate, could tell.

What C.S. Lewis called the 'snobbery of chronology' encourages us to presume that just because we happen to have lived after our ancestors and can read books which give us some account of what happened to them, we must also know better than them. We certainly have more facts at our disposal. We have more wealth, both personal and national, better technology, and infinitely more skilful ways of preserving and extending our lives. But whether we today display more wisdom or common humanity is an open question, and as we look back to discover how people coped with the daily difficulties of existence a thousand years ago, we might also consider whether, in all our sophistication, we could meet the challenges of their world with the same fortitude, good humour, and philosophy.

The Year 1000 by Robert Lacey and Danny Danziger will be published by Little, Brown.

from The Drowning People

by Richard Mason

Richard Mason is twenty-one years old and is studying English at Oxford. There follows an extract from his first novel. What has driven James Farrell to murder his wife of forty years in cold blood?

I am in the little sitting room (in days gone by a dressing room) that connects my bedroom to Sarah's. It is the warmest room in this icy house because it is the smallest. With both doors closed and a fire blazing and the radiators on under its pointed Gothic windows, it is almost cosy. There is no desk in here, only a sofa and two chairs and a small table covered with books. Old books; my favourite books; their inscriptions faded, their givers dead. They have sat on that table for more than forty years, I should think: a Bible, calf-bound, from my mother; my grandfather's *Fowler's*; Donne's love poetry, an old edition of Ella's borrowed long ago. There is a music stand in the corner too, hardly used now; a graduation gift from my parents. From where I sit I can see my initials engraved on its base: *For J.H.F. June 1994*. June 1994; almost fifty years ago. That stand was mine before I ever knew her.

It seems suddenly important to me that I should have explained myself to myself by the time everyone arrives. I need clarity. The coroner's inquest is set for tomorrow; then there'll be the funeral and the interment and the house will be full of people. From this evening on I shan't have a moment's peace for weeks; no time to myself in which to think. If ever I am to put the events of my life in some sort of order I must begin the sifting now; I must try, I know, to understand what I have done; to understand how I, at the age of seventy, have come to kill my wife and to feel so little remorse over it.

It is curious, my lack of compunction; not complete, perhaps, but almost. Now that Sarah is gone, now that I know the truth, I feel very little. Hardly any outright regret. Just a curious, empty, almost eerie, calm: a numbness that shows me, perhaps, quite how much I have learned from her. Quietly, detached, I sit here alone; and it strikes me that in some ways I should be glad, though I am not; that the absence of gladness is a striking one, for years ago this knowledge would have freed me. It would have given me what some call a new lease of life; I might have gone back. So it is odd that I should feel nothing now, or at most next to nothing. The events of those weeks and months long ago, in which the seeds of it all were sown, have a play-like quality. I know the plot and can empathize with the characters; but the young man of twenty-two who plays such a central part is a stranger to me. He bears little relation (beyond a slight, decreasing, physical similarity) to the image that confronts me as I pass the looking glass by the fireplace; as I stare at the books, at the music stand, at the waves and the gun-grey sky.

My life seems to have slowed. The present takes up so much time. I see myself as I was at twenty-two. Young, very young, a certain physical gangliness characterizing my movements (I was tall, with long legs) and a small nose, delicate like my mother's. My mouth is thin-lipped; my eyes a pale brown; and all are set in a regular oval face with small ears and a slightly pointed chin. Hardly handsome, I suppose; and at that age undignified by the lines of age. My face is more careworn now; the years have creased and folded it. But that is as it should be.

I suppose that my family life and upbringing must go some way to explaining why my adult life has turned out as it has, why I have turned out as I have. Ella's shoulders are too fragile to bear the complete weight of the responsibility, as are mine. Perhaps it is time to exhume old ghosts, to see my parents as they were in their forties and fifties: my mother, with her dark hair greying and her piercing blue eyes, so shrewd and voluble; my father with his powerful shoulders and huge veined hands. He was a man of deliberate gesture and unshakeable self-belief, a quality I don't think he ever succeeded in passing on to me. What he did give me, and it is this for which I thank my family most, is stubbornness: for it has sustained me when all else has failed, when arrogance and self-belief have deserted me.

What did my parents want for me? What were they like? It is so difficult to know, so difficult to give complete answers to any questions like these. We were not rich, I know that much, but we knew rich people (which my mother felt, and once or twice almost said, was enough). And I suppose that my parents, like any parents, hoped that their son would go far in the world. In *their* world, I should say; for they lived, like so many of their class and generation, in comfortable, unquestioning calm, unruffled by external change. My parents did not look outwards. They never ventured beyond the range of their own ambition, being serenely confident – in a way which frequently infuriated me – of their place in the order of things. Their gods were tradition, propriety, the maintenance of the social hierarchy. They looked both up and down; were deferential to those above and polite to those beneath; they read *The Times*, voted Conservative and held unchanging and predictable views on the events of the day. The revolutions of the 1960s had done nothing to unsettle their values or to disturb their quiet hopes; and because they were kind they insisted on planning my future on their own terms and with all the tenacity of challenged sincerity.

My own private plan of becoming a concert violinist, flatly and sullenly expressed in my last year at Oxford, could have met with no favour in their eyes; nor did it. And my late adolescence was punctuated occasionally, but always dramatically, by the slow build-up of family tension, its explosive release and its subsequent subsidence over long days of icy politeness.

It is ironic that I should end my life in a house like this one, with a titled wife whose family history is as weighty as any to which her parents-in-law could ever have aspired. It is ironic that, having made so much of following my own lights, I have succeeded ultimately in achieving only what my parents wished for me all along. My musical career died gradually as my marriage progressed, for Sarah could not hope to fuel it as Ella had done, nor did she try to; and my reserves of emotion have dwindled unavoidably over time. My talent lay in translating private passion into public performance, and as the private passion stopped flowing, dried, and finally turned to a dust so fine that the slightest wind scattered it to nothingness, there was no longer anything to be translated. Technically I remained pre-eminent, for I have always been diligent; but I stopped playing when I could hope for nothing more than mechanical brilliance.

But I am wandering, losing the flow of my narrative. It is only to be expected from a man of my age, I suppose.

My education was unremarkable. I was clever enough to join the majority of my public-school fellows at Oxford, a great relief to my parents; and until the age of nineteen I made a creditable enough return on their investment in me. But over the three years of my separation from my family at university I was encouraged by those I knew and the books I read to cultivate a certain detachment from home life and its aspirations for me, a detachment which made me critical during term time and superior in the holidays. It was then that I turned with real determination to my secret love, the violin; and it was then, comparatively late but in time enough, that I had the leisure and the teaching to discover that I might be really good; good enough to matter. Good enough, certainly, to use my music as the basis for my first serious confrontation with my parents, one which raged the whole of the summer following my graduation and that centred around my stubborn insistence that I was going to be a musician.

But I digress in my attempt to make my twenty-two-year-old self more real to me now, an attempt in which I have been only partly successful. I remember once more what he looks like, that is true; I see his half-smile and his rosy cheeks and the hair tumbling over his forehead into his eyes. But I know him no longer; I have no empathy with his tastes and only a little with his enthusiasms, surprisingly few of which have remained. I struggle to remember the people with whom he filled his life, the friendships he made: curiously intense, for he was a young man of extremes, inclined to manic sociability and profound gloom by turns. Of course, a few stand distinct from the tableau. People like Camilla Boardman, the girl my mother always hoped I would marry: pretty; bubbly; well-connected; more substantial than she liked to seem. But I was insular at twenty-two. Indiscriminately friendly, I shared myself intimately with great discrimination; I still do. Perhaps I had little to share; certainly my life up to that point contained nothing very remarkable. I had made the progression from preparatory school to public school to Oxford with as few jolts as possible; I had not forced myself to think much or to examine the world. Life was as it was and I accepted it on its own terms, much in the way I would later accept my marriage to Sarah: with a sort of dogged determination which I would not admit to myself.

Unthinking, unseeing, unknowing, I drifted through life until I met Ella. It was she who baptized me; it was she who threw me into the sea of life. And she did it quite unthinkingly, little caring or even knowing how much good or how much harm she might do. It was in her nature, that wild abandonment, that driving need for experience and explanation. It was she who made me swim, she who pushed me from the safety of the shallows; it was she with whom I floundered, out of my depth. It is to her, and to my memories of her, that I must turn now in seeking to explain what I have done.

The Drowning People *by Richard Mason will be published by Michael Joseph.*

from Nathaniel's Nutmeg

by Giles Milton

> Nathaniel's Nutmeg *is the story of the seventeenth-century spice-trader Nathaniel Courthope whose courage in the Spice Islands led to the founding of the greatest city on earth – Manhattan.*

Scarcely had Lancaster's vessels reached the Thames Estuary than the wind dropped and for almost two months the sails hung loose. It was not until Easter that his fleet finally reached Dartmouth. Delayed again at Torbay, Lancaster sent instructions to each of the ships, listing ports and harbours where they should rendezvous in the event of becoming separated. And then, with the wind once more filling their sails, the ships set off down the English Channel and had an uneventful passage all the way to Gran Canaria.

Here, the wind again died and for more than a month the fleet floated idly at sea, inching slowly towards the equator. Just two degrees short of the line Lancaster had a stroke of good fortune. A lone Portuguese ship, accidentally separated from her accompanying carracks, was spied on the horizon. The five English vessels circled her then closed for the kill. She was boarded, her crew disarmed and a team of men sent down into the hold. She proved to be a very rich prize: she was laden with 146 butts of wine and 176 jars of oil and her captured cargo was shared out among the English ships according to the number of men on board. And then, without further ado, they set sail once again.

As with Lancaster's first voyage, men began to fall sick as soon as they crossed into the southern hemisphere and it was not long before 'the weakness of men was so great that in some of the ships the merchants took their turn at the helm and went into the top to take in the topsails'. But while men grew weaker on the smaller vessels, the diarist on board Lancaster's *Red Dragon* could not help noticing that her crew were completely immune to the illness. 'And the reason why the general's men stood in better health than the men of other ships was this; he [Lancaster] brought to sea with him certain bottles of the juice of lemons, which he gave to each one, as long as it would last, three spoonfuls every morning, fasting; not suffering them to eat anything after it till noon . . . by this means the general cured many of his men and preserved the rest.' How Lancaster stumbled upon the cure for scurvy remains a mystery; it may be that he noticed the spectacular recovery that men made as soon as they were able to add fresh fruit and vegetables to their diet of salted food. On his first voyage the on-board chronicler Henry May had observed that one particularly ill crew member had made a full recovery after eating the oranges and lemons found on St Helena. Tragically, Lancaster's cure was soon forgotten and more than 170 years were to pass before Captain Cook rediscovered the beneficial effects of citrus fruit in combating scurvy.

Although scurvy and sickness were a constant concern, life on board had its lighter moments. Journals and diaries make frequent mention of the play-acting, singing and clowning around that enlivened the tedium of the voyage. Music was extremely popular and on one vessel 'a virginal was brought for two to play upon at once'. This proved a great success, for no sooner had the music commenced than 'the jacks skip up and down in such a manner as they will'. A later expedition even boasted a cornet player who used to regularly play for his colleagues. So accomplished was he at the instrument, and so wide was his repertoire, that on arriving in India he found himself blowing his brass for the Great Moghul himself.

The merry-making was helped along by the huge quantities of alcohol consumed by the crew. Although attempts were made to regulate the drinking, it was universally ignored until men began to drop dead of liver disorders caused by the 'inordinate drinking of a wine called tastie [toddy] distilled from the palmetto tree'.

After merry-making their way across the southern Atlantic, Lancaster's expedition finally slipped into South Africa's Table Bay on 9 September 1601, where the commander knew he could barter for fresh meat and provisions. As had happened on his first voyage, the crew viewed the natives as wild barbarians who were laughably easy to exploit. Neither side was able to communicate with the other, for 'their speech is wholly uttered through the throat, and they cluck with their tongues in such sort that, in seven weeks which we remained here in this place, the sharpest wit among us could not learn one word of their language'.

Instead, the English sailors 'spake to them in the cattle's language'. When they wanted to buy oxen they would say 'moo'. When they wanted sheep, they would say 'baa'. The animals cost next to nothing: the natives did not demand silver or gold but seemed content with a couple of old iron hoops. After twelve days, the ship's company had bought more than a thousand sheep and several dozen oxen.

When his ships finally set sail, Lancaster must have been pleased that his time in Table Bay had passed without incident. Aware that this was an essential revictualling point for ships heading east he did everything possible to ensure that negotiations with the natives progressed smoothly. Such a policy was in stark contrast to that of Cornelis Houtman who had treated the natives of southern Africa with brutality and paid for it with the loss of thirteen crew.

Although every inch of space on the vessels was taken up with fresh supplies, the hot southern climate was still taking its toll on the crew and it was decided to land at the island of Cirne – now known as Mauritius – where lemons were said to be plentiful. Unfortunately, the wind unexpectedly changed direction and the little fleet was blown towards Madagascar instead. Arriving on Christmas Day in the bay of Atongill, a reconnaissance party discovered a series of carvings on a rock close to the water. It had long been the practice to carve upon rocks the dates of arrival and departure of ships so that straggling vessels might know the fate of the rest of their fleet. From these carvings, Lancaster discovered to his dismay that five Dutch ships had called here just two months earlier. They had lost more than two hundred men to dysentery while they lay at anchor.

History soon began to repeat itself on the English ships. First the *Red Dragon*'s master's mate died, then the preacher, the surgeon, and ten crew members. Others suffered more violent deaths: as the master's mate was lowered into the ground, the captain of the *Ascension* rowed ashore to attend the funeral. While doing so, he had the misfortune to enter the line of musket shot that was frequently fired on such occasions and both he and the boatswain's mate were killed, 'so that they that went to see the buriall of another', records the ship's diarist, 'and were both buried there themselves'.

It was a most unfortunate accident; Captain William Brund was popular among the sea dogs he commanded and was sorely missed. His death reinforced the growing feeling that Madagascar was not a place to linger, so as soon as the *Red Dragon*'s little pinnace had been assembled (it was brought out from England in kit form) the fleet once more set sail.

The expanse of the Indian Ocean presented Lancaster with fewer problems than the Atlantic. A near-catastrophe was avoided when the pinnace detected the reefs and shoals surrounding the Chagos Archipelago and by the second week of May the ships had caught sight of the remote Nicobar Islands – missed on Lancaster's first voyage – where they resolved to revictual. To their surprise they discovered that the fantastical writings of medieval travellers, which spoke of men with horns and green faces, appeared to be correct. According to the ship's journal, the island priest 'had upon his head a pair of horns turning backward', while others had 'their faces painted green, black, and yellow, and their horns also painted with the same colour; and behind them, upon their buttocks, a tail hanging down, very much like the manner as in some painted clothes we paint the devil in our country'.

It is ironic that just as sceptics in England were beginning to question the veracity of accounts by medieval 'explorers' like Sir John Mandeville, genuine travellers were reporting sights that bore witness to their more outlandish tales. Sir Walter Raleigh was one of those sceptics who changed his opinion of Mandeville after hearing the reports filtering back from the mysterious East. 'Mandeville's reports were holden for fables many yeeres,' he wrote, 'and yet since the East Indies were discovered, we find his relations true of such things as heretofore were held incredible.'

On 5 June 1602, more than sixteen months after leaving Woolwich, Lancaster's fleet finally arrived at the Sumatran port of Achin.

Nathaniel's Nutmeg *by Giles Milton will be published by Hodder & Stoughton.*

from Tulip Fever

by Deborah Moggach

*Deborah Moggach's last two novels were dramatized by
the BBC and Channel 4. Now comes her most accomplished novel to date, an exquisitely crafted story of art
and illusion, doomed love and a tulip, set in seventeenth-
century Amsterdam.*

Cornelis

Two weeks pass before the next sitting. Cornelis is a
busy man, he is always out and about. He has his
warehouse to run, down in the harbour. At midday the
Stock Market opens and he hurries down to the Bourse.
Amsterdam is awash with capital and dealing there is
brisk, often frenzied, because the place closes at two. In
addition to this he has civic duties for he is a prominent
citizen, a man of substance in this burgeoning city. It is
1636 and Amsterdam is thriving. The seat of govern-
ment is in The Hague, but Amsterdam is the true capital
of the Republic. Trade is booming; the arts are flourish-
ing. Fashionable men and women stroll along its streets
and the canals mirror back the handsome houses in
which they live. The city is threaded with mirrors. They
reflect the cold spring sunshine. Copper-coloured clouds
lie motionless beneath the bridges. The city sees itself in
its own water like a woman gazing into a looking-glass.

Can we not forgive vanity in one so beautiful?

And hanging in a thousand homes, paintings mirror back the lives that are lived here. A woman plays the virginal; she catches the eye of the man beside her. A handsome young soldier lifts a glass to his lips; his reflection shines in the silver-topped decanter. A maid gives her mistress a letter . . . The mirrored moments are stilled, suspended in aspic. For centuries to come people will gaze at these paintings and wonder what is about to happen. That letter, what does it say to the woman who stands at the window, the sunlight streaming on to her face? Is she in love? Will she throw away the letter or will she obey it, waiting until the house is empty and stealing out through the rooms that recede, bathed in shafts of sunshine, at the back of the painting?

Who can tell? For her face is serene, her secrets locked into her heart. She stands there, trapped in her frame, poised at a moment of truth. She has yet to make her decision.

Sophia stands at a window. She has not seen Cornelis approach. She is standing halfway up the stairs. The window-panes are tinted glass – amber and blood-red. In the centre is painted a bird trapped in foliage. She cannot see out. The sun shines through, suffusing her face with colour. She stands there, utterly still.

Cornelis thinks: she is already a painting – here, now, before she has been immortalized on canvas. Then he feels an odd sensation. His wife has vanished, her soul sucked away, and just her outward form remains in its cobalt-blue dress.

'My love—' he says.

She jumps, and swings round.

'Did you not hear the knock at the door? Mr van Loos is here, he is waiting downstairs.'

Her hand flies to her hair. 'He's here?'

Cornelis has placed a vase of tulips on the table. He has

asked for it to be included in the painting for tulips are a passion of his.

'I bought these at some expense,' he says. 'They are *tulipa clusiana*, forced under glass. That is why we can enjoy them at this early season. They were grown by the Portuguese Jew Francisco Gomez da Costa.' The white petals are flushed with pink. 'It is no wonder, is it, that a poet compared them with the faint blush on the cheek of chaste Susannah?' He clears his throat. 'Do they not remind us of the transitory nature of beauty, how that which is lovely must one day die?'

'Perhaps that's why we should grasp it while we can,' says the painter.

There is a silence. Sophia shifts in her seat.

'I hardly think you would find *that* teaching in our Scriptures.' Cornelis clears his throat again. Painters are known to be godless, disreputable fellows. 'Besides, I have found my heaven on earth.' Cornelis feels a rush of love for his wife. He leans down and touches her cheek.

'Don't move!' says the painter sharply. 'Return to your position please.'

Cornelis, stung, puts his hand back on his hip. Sometimes he gets carried away and forgets that he is having his portrait painted. But it is hard work. Standing still makes his back ache.

Jan van Loos stands behind his easel. He paints noiselessly. The sound of brushing comes from the next room, where Maria is sweeping the floor.

'Is it not strange, this madness that has gripped us?' asks Cornelis.

'What madness?' asks the painter.

'Have you surrendered to this passion yet?'

The painter pauses. 'It depends what passion you are talking about.'

'This speculation on tulip bulbs.'

'Ah.' The painter smiles. 'Tulip bulbs.'

111

Beside Cornelis, his wife shifts in her seat again. Cornelis decides that this painter is somewhat slow-witted. 'I thought we were a sober people,' he says, 'but over the past two years we have become a nation possessed.'

'So I have heard.'

'And it has enslaved people from all ranks – turf cutters and barge skippers, butchers and bakers. Maybe painters too.'

'Not me,' replies the painter. 'I know nothing of business.'

'Ah, nor do they. But great fortunes have been made and lost. These new hybrids that they have been growing – they fetch the most astonishing prices. Thousands of florins, if you know when to buy and sell.' Cornelis's voice rises with excitement; he too has greatly profited from this tulipomania. 'Why, one Semper Augustus bulb – they are the most beautiful and the most valuable – one bulb was sold last week for six fine horses, three oxheads of wine, a dozen sheep, two dozen silver goblets and a seascape by Esaias van de Velde!'

The painter raises his eyebrows and carries on working. A petal drops, like a shed skirt, from one of the tulips. It lies on the table. Sweep ... sweep ... goes Maria's broom. They can hear her humming.

There is a drowsy, drugged atmosphere in the room. Cornelis suddenly feels alone, as if he is travelling in a coach and everyone else has fallen asleep. Why doesn't his wife respond?

'It is not a native plant, of course – it comes from Turkey. When I was a young man the tulip was known only to the *cognoscenti* – aristocrats and horticulturalists. But we are a green-fingered, resourceful people, are we not? And, nourished by our rich soil the humble bulb has been developed into ever-richer and more spectacular varieties. No wonder people have been losing grip of their senses, for even in death a tulip is beautiful. Your own colleagues have immortalized them on canvas – the

Bosschaert brothers, Jan Davidsz de Heem – pictures of astonishing realism which, unlike the flowers they depict, will continue to bloom for generations to come—'

'Please stop talking,' says Jan. 'I'm trying to paint your mouth.'

Sophia makes a snuffling sound. She is laughing. She stops, quickly.

Cornelis's skin stings, as if he has been slapped. Where is the respect? He has so much to teach his wife, so many years of experience in the world. Sometimes he suspects that her attention is wandering. She is so young – such a pretty creature but her head is full of nonsense. He suddenly misses his first wife, Hendrijke. How solid and reliable she was. Hendrijke never set his blood on fire, he never felt for her what he feels for Sophia, but she was a true companion. Sophia is so moody – one minute loving, the next distracted and skittish. For the past few days she has been acting quite strangely.

He sets his face in a stern expression. He puffs out his chest and grips his cane. He is not entirely sure that he likes this fellow. Sophia herself had voiced her doubts. But they have started; they had better go through with it.

The Painting

Jan van Loos is not painting the old man's mouth. He is painting Sophia's lips. He mixes pink on his palette – ochre, grey and carmine – and strokes the paint lovingly on the canvas. She is gazing at him. For a moment, when the old man was talking, her lips curved into a smile – a smile of complicity. He paints the ghost of this, though it is now gone.

There is no sound in the house. The painting, when it is finished, will look the most tranquil of scenes. Downstairs, Maria has fallen asleep. Exhausted by love she snoozes on a chair in the kitchen. Willem crept into her bed, the night before, and crept out at dawn. As she

113

sleeps the tom-cat drags a plaice across the floor. He too does this noiselessly. The small theft is detected by nobody.

Upstairs, something else is being stolen. Cornelis, too, is drowsy. Sunshine pours through the library window. There is a stone chimney-piece here, supported by caryatids. The sun bathes their breasts. The fossils wait, through centuries of waiting.

Half an hour passes. The painter has scarcely touched his canvas. He is gazing at Sophia. Behind her, on the wall, hangs a *Descent from the Cross*. It is an Italian painting, by the school of Caravaggio. Christ is being lowered. Light illuminates his naked torso. He is no pale, passive, Northern Christ. He is a real man – broad shoulders, muscles, ropes of veins. He has suffered and been slaughtered. The weight of him, upended, fills the frame. He seems to be sliding down on the heads of the couple below.

Beneath Christ stands the old man, the patriarch, his chest thrust out above his spindly legs. His face, cushioned by his ruff, dares the viewer to question his fitness as one of God's chosen. Beside him sits his beautiful young wife. Her hair is pulled back demurely from her face but pearls glint within it, winking at the viewer. They tell a different story. On her lips there is the faintest smile. For whom is she smiling, the painter or the viewer? And is it really a smile at all?

Cornelis is talking but nobody listens. Sophia and the painter gaze at each other with a terrible seriousness. Another petal falls; it reveals the firm knob of the stigma.

Jan starts to paint. The disrobed tulip, in the painting, will be back in full bloom. Centuries later people will stand in the Rijksmuseum and gaze at this canvas. What will they see? Tranquillity, harmony. A married couple who, though surrounded by wealth, are aware that this life is swiftly over (the scales, the skull). Maybe the old man was talking, but he is silent now. They didn't listen then and now nobody can hear.

His young wife is indeed beautiful. Her gaze is candid and full of love. The blush remains in her cheek but she has perished, long ago. Only the painting remains.

Tulip Fever *by Deborah Moggach will be published by William Heinemann.*

from Dancing Naked in the Mind Field

by Kary Mullis

Kary Mullis was born in North Carolina in 1944 and attended the Georgia Institute of Technology. In 1993 Dr Mullis was awarded the Nobel Prize and the Japan Prize for his invention of the polymerase chain reaction (PCR).

In December of 1992 I had agreed to head a project based on a concept of mine that, if it worked, would change the world of medical diagnostics. Two German pharmaceutical companies had agreed to provide our company, Atomic Tags, with $6 million to start working on it in California. They would expect me to continue directing it. I figured it would take ten years, with a staff of a hundred chemists, physicists, and physicians. The research would cost maybe $30 million a year once we got up and running, but if it worked, it would be well worth it. Unfortunately, I would be responsible for it. You foolish person, I thought as I flew back to California, you've let these two businessmen talk you into making them a bunch of money. But I had committed myself.

Waiting for me when I returned home was a letter from the Japanese Ministry of Technology informing me that I had been awarded the Japan Prize. Fifty million yen. It was 1:30 a.m. and I had no idea what the exchange rate was for the yen. I spent the night wondering whether I was rich. In the morning I found out it was about

$375,000. I could live a long time on that.

The Germans dropped a bomb just two weeks later on my ten-year research project. The Bundestadt passed a new law that diminished the profits of the German pharmaceutical companies by about thirty per cent. That cut out any new foreign research. Atomic Tags turned belly up and I was free.

With a light heart, I was off to Japan to meet the emperor and the empress. I might be the only person ever to address the empress of Japan as 'sweetie'. She was kind enough not to chastize me for it. I had fun talking to her. I asked her how many other empresses she knew. She said there were only three in the world. I asked her who the other two were, and we agreed that they were not potential girl friends. 'So you don't have any girl friends?'

She said without hesitation, 'No girl friends.'

Dancing Naked in the Mind Field *by Kary Mullis was published by Bloomsbury.*

from Soup and Beyond: Soups, Beans and Other Things

New Covent Garden Soup Company

Soup and Beyond: Soup, Beans and Other Things *by the New Covent Garden Soup Company will be published by Macmillan.*

Carrot & Cardamom Soup

Ⓥ Ⓕ

In 1988 we sold our first fresh soup, Carrot & Coriander. 11 years and 50 million carrots later it is still our best-selling recipe. Last year, to mark our 10th birthday, we produced this new sophisticated version with the seeds of cardamom pods used extensively in Arabia and India for their subtle flavour.

The inspiration came during a marketing department lunch at the newly opened Putney Bridge restaurant in London. Alison Adcock, following her tradition of eating soup every day of the year, was tempted by the Carrot & Cardamom on the menu. The combination was so delicious she rushed back to the factory, created the recipe for a lighter version, and the new soup was born.

SERVES: 4
PREPARATION AND COOKING TIME: 50 minutes

30g (1oz) butter
1 large onion, finely chopped
1 garlic clove, crushed
450g (1lb) (approx. 6) carrots, peeled and cut into equal size chunks
1 level tablespoon plain flour
850ml (1½ pints) vegetable stock
15g (½oz) creamed coconut
1 tablespoon lemon juice
seeds of 8 cardamom pods, crushed with a pestle & mortar
1 teaspoon sugar
salt and freshly ground black pepper

TO GARNISH:

toasted coconut shavings
cook fresh coconut shavings quickly in a dry pan

Melt the butter and cook the onion, garlic and carrots gently in a large covered saucepan for 5 minutes, without colouring. Add the flour and cook gently for 2 minutes. Stir in the stock, creamed coconut and lemon juice. Cover, bring to the boil and simmer gently for about 15 minutes until the carrots are tender. Cool a little, then purée in a liquidiser until smooth. Add the cardamom and sugar and season to taste. Reheat gently and serve with a twist of black pepper or chill and serve ice-cold. Garnish with toasted coconut shavings.

from What Every Kid Wished Their Parents Knew . . . and vice versa!

by Rob Parsons and Lloyd Parsons

*'My mother's an alien!' . . . 'My kids are from Mars!'
For every parent who longs to get inside their kids' heads
and for all kids who need to understand what makes their
parents tick, comes a book from a father and son team
that will have you laughing, crying and yelling, 'It's not
just us!'*

Rob on a man that every parent hates

Son, you can help me with something that's been
troubling me for years. I'm sure it's no big deal but it is
eating away at me and it's best we sort it out. It's just
that on the very day you hit eleven, another person
emerged in our relationship. I call him 'Everybody else's
father'.

I first came across him when you wanted to sleep
over at Billy's house. I had never heard of Billy and
frankly there was precious little information forthcoming
from you. For all I knew a sleep-over at Billy's could
have been in the same category as a night on the town
in Beirut. I said, 'No.' And it was then that the
character who was, henceforth, to make regular appear-
ances in our lives stepped out of the shadows. You burst
into tears and said, 'Everybody else's father is letting
them go.'

120

You slept over at Billy's.

Since that fateful day this character has poked his nose into just about every conflict you and I have ever had. 'Everybody else's father lets his child go to a disco the evening before the GCSE maths exam.' 'Everybody else's father lets his offspring have his ear, nose and belly button pierced.' And 'everybody else's father' gives his kids amounts of pocket money that make me look like I need a visit from Marley's ghost.

The strange thing is that although I thought I had met the parents of all of your friends, I have still not come across this man in the flesh. In fact, so far as I can tell, all the other parents are just about as scared, mingy and boring as me.

So here's the deal for the future. Next time you resort to using this character, I'll agree to whatever you want so long as you produce him. I mean real, live 'everybody else's father' in my living room. And even if that means I have to agree to your going poker-playing in Las Vegas for a year, it'll be worth it.

And when you're gone and there's just me and 'everybody else's father', I'm going to ring every parent I've ever met and tell them I've caught the guy, he's locked in my garage and dying to meet us all . . .

Lloyd on Things You Wish Your Parents Would Say

Would you like to borrow the car? I just filled it up.

Why don't you get your nose pierced at the same time?

We're out Saturday night – why don't you have a party?

I trust you.

If we remove that desk from your bedroom, we could get a wide-screen telly in.

You're one of a kind.

Well done, you did great.

Ten pounds is not enough, come on, take twenty.

Why don't you start a band?

OK, so you've made a few mistakes, but we're still proud to be your parents.

Hang on, those jeans need another rip.

What Every Kid Wished their Parents Knew . . . and vice versa! *by Rob Parsons and Lloyd Parsons will be published by Hodder & Stoughton.*

from The Tulip

by Anna Pavord

Anna Pavord is the gardening correspondent for the
Independent, *and the author of widely praised gardening
books including* The Flowering Year *and* The Gardening Companion. *She lives in Dorset, England, in an old
rectory with a large garden.*

By the middle of the eighteenth century, florists' societies,
devoted to the culture of a particular group of flowers,
had been established all over England. Early newspaper
advertisements for florists' 'feasts' were replaced by news
of shows, such as the tulip show held at the White Horse,
Bury St Edmunds, where 'lovers of these amiable bulbs'
could win a silver punch ladle for the best bloom. But
since it was usually pubs, such as the White Horse, the
Golden Cock Inn, Kirkgate, Leeds, the Shears Inn, Lee
Bridge, Halifax, or the Crown Inn, Nottingham, which
offered convenient meeting rooms for the tulip shows,
carousing continued just the same. The arrangement
suited both parties: the florists got a venue at a minimal
sum and the landlord sold vast quantities of ale. Some
severe florists in Newcastle pointed out that *their* show
was 'a Source of Delight and not of Extravagance and
Luxury, which was the only Rock former societies of this
sort split upon'. Fortunately, in the larger manufacturing
towns, rival shows were common and Newcastle florists

with a thirst would find themselves well catered for by Mr James Beech at the Rising Sun.

In the hundred years between 1750 and 1850, scarcely any town of importance in the north of England was without its tulip show. Members of the Ancient Society of York Florists, founded in 1768, brought hyacinths, polyanthus and auriculas to their spring display, which ended with a feast. Tulips were shown separately in May. The Botanic Society of Manchester held its first tulip meeting on 20 May 1777 and the Rev. William Hanbury (1725-1778), rector of Church Langton, Leicestershire, wrote that 'the florists are now become more numerous in England than has been known in any preceding age . . . many clubs have been founded and feasts established, when premiums are allowed the best and fairest. These feasts are now become general, and are regularly held at towns, at proper distance almost all over England. At these exhibitions, let not the Gardeners be dejected if a weaver runs away with the prize, as is often done.'

The Tulip *by Anna Pavord was published by Bloomsbury.*

from The Last Continent

by Terry Pratchett

In his latest novel in the phenomenally successful Disc-world series, Terry Pratchett takes the reader to the hot, dry lands of EcksEcksEcksEcks, The Last Continent – *a place that is emphatically not Australia, it's just vaguely Australian.*

Through an unfortunate error in bi-locational thau-maturgy, Rincewind, one-time Deputy Librarian at Ankh-Morpork's Unseen University, had been sent to Discworld's little-known continent EcksEcksEcks-Ecks – and he'd rather be anywhere else at all . . .

After his nourishing meal that contained masses of essential vitamins and minerals and unfortunately quite a lot of taste as well, the man with 'Wizzard' on his hat settled down for some housekeeping, or as much as was possible in the absence of a house.

It consisted of chipping away at a piece of wood with a stone axe. He appeared to be making a very short plank, and the speed with which he was working suggested that he'd done this before.

A cockatoo settled in the tree above him to watch. Rincewind glared at it suspiciously.

When the plank had apparently been smoothed to his satisfaction he stood on it with one foot and, swaying, drew around the foot with a piece of charcoal from the fire. He did the same with the other foot, and then settled down to hack at the wood again.

The watcher in the waterhole realized that the man was making two foot-shaped boards.

Rincewind took a length of twine from his pocket. He'd found a particular creeper which, if you carefully peeled the bark off, would give you a terrible spotted rash. What he'd actually been *looking* for was a creeper which, if you carefully peeled off the bark, would give you a serviceable twine, and it had taken several more goes and various different rashes to find out which one this was.

If you made a hole in the soles and fed a loop of twine through it, into which a toe could be inserted, you ended up with some Ur-footwear. It made you shuffle like the Ascent of Man but, nevertheless, had some unexpected benefits. First, the steady flop-flop as you walked made you sound like *two* people to any dangerous creatures you were about to encounter, which, in Rincewind's recent experience, was any creature at all. Second, although they were impossible to run *in*, they were easy to run *out* of, so that you were a smoking dot on the burning horizon while the enraged caterpillar or beetle was still looking at your shoes and wondering where the other person was.

He'd had to run away a lot. Every night he made a new pair of thonged sandals, and every day he left them somewhere in the desert.

When he'd finished them to his satisfaction he took a roll of thin bark from his pocket. Attached to it by a length of twine was a very precious small stub of pencil. He'd decided to keep a journal in the hope that this might help. He looked at the recent entries.

Probably Tuesday: hot, flies. Dinner: honey ants. Attacked by honey ants. Fell into waterhole.
Wednesday, with any luck: hot, flies. Dinner: either bush raisins or kangaroo droppings. Chased by hunters, don't know why. Fell into waterhole.

Thursday (could be): hot, flies. Dinner: blue-tongued lizard. Savaged by blue-tongued lizard. Chased by different hunters. Fell off cliff, bounced into tree, pissed on by small grey incontinent teddy bear, landed in a waterhole.

Friday: hot, flies. Dinner: some kind of roots which tasted like sick. This saved time.

Saturday: hotter than yesterday, extra flies. V. thirsty.

Sunday: hot. Delirious with thirst and flies. Nothing but nothing as far as the eye can see, with bushes in it. Decided to die, collapsed, fell down sand dune into waterhole.

He wrote very carefully and as small as possible: '*Monday:* hot, flies. Dinner: moth grubs.' He stared at the writing. It said it all, really.

Why didn't people here like him? He'd meet some small tribe, everything'd be friendly, he'd pick up a few tips, get to know a few names, he'd build up a vocabulary, enough to chat about ordinary everyday things like the weather – and then suddenly they'd be chasing him away. After all, *everyone* talked about the weather, didn't they?

Rincewind had always been happy to think of himself as a racist. The One Hundred Metres, the Mile, the Marathon – he'd run them all. Later, when he'd learned with some surprise what the word actually *meant*, he'd been equally certain he wasn't one. He was a person who divided the world quite simply into people who were trying to kill him and people who weren't. That didn't leave much room for fine details like what colour anyone was. But he'd be sitting by the campfire, trying out a simple conversation, and suddenly people would get upset over nothing at all and drive him off. You didn't expect people to get nasty just because you'd said something like, 'My word, when did it last rain here?' did you?

Rincewind sighed, picked up his stick, beat the hell out

of a patch of ground, lay down and went to sleep.

Occasionally he screamed under his breath and his legs made running motions, which just showed that he was dreaming.

The waterhole rippled. It wasn't large, a mere puddle deep in a bush-filled gully between some rocks, and the liquid it contained could only be called water because geographers refuse to countenance words like 'souphole'.

Nevertheless it rippled, as though something had dropped into the centre. And what was odd about the ripples was that they didn't stop when they reached the edge of the water but continued outwards over the land as expanding circles of dim white light. When they reached Rincewind they broke up and flowed around him, so that now he was the centre of concentric lines of white dots, like strings of pearls.

The waterhole erupted. *Something* climbed up into the air and sped away across the night.

It zigzagged from rock to mountain to waterhole. And as the eye of observation rises, the travelling streak briefly illuminates other dim lines, hanging above the ground like smoke, so from above the whole land appears to have a circulatory system, or nerves . . .

A thousand miles from the sleeping wizard the line struck ground again, emerged in a cave, and passed across the walls like a searchlight.

It hovered in front of a huge, pointed rock for a moment and then, as if reaching a decision, shot up again into the sky.

The continent rolled below it as it returned. The light hit the waterhole without a splash but, once again, three or four ripples in *something* spread out across the turbid water and the surrounding sand.

Night rolled in again. But there was a distant thumping under the ground. Bushes trembled. In the trees, birds awoke and flew away.

After a while, on a rock face near the waterhole, pale white lines began to form a picture.

Rincewind had attracted the attention of at least one other watcher apart from whatever it was that dwelt in the waterhole.

Death had taken to keeping Rincewind's lifetimer on a special shelf in his study, in much the way that a zoologist would want to keep an eye on a particularly intriguing specimen.

The lifetimers of most people were the classic shape that Death thought was right and proper for the task. They appeared to be large eggtimers, although, since the sands they measured were the living seconds of someone's life, all the eggs were in one basket.

Rincewind's hourglass looked like something created by a glassblower who'd had the hiccups in a time machine. According to the amount of actual sand it contained – and Death was pretty good at making this kind of estimate – he should have died long ago. But strange curves and bends and extrusions of glass had developed over the years, and quite often the sand was flowing backwards, or diagonally. Clearly, Rincewind had been hit by so much magic, had been thrust reluctantly through time and space so often that he'd nearly bumped into himself coming the other way, that the precise end of his life was now as hard to find as the starting point on a roll of really sticky transparent tape.

Death was familiar with the concept of the eternal, ever-renewed hero, the champion with a thousand faces. He'd refrained from commenting. He met heroes frequently, generally surrounded by, and this was important, the dead bodies of *very nearly* all their enemies and saying, 'Vot the hell shust happened?' Whether there was some arrangement that allowed them to come back again afterwards was not something he would be drawn on.

But he pondered whether, if this creature *did* exist, it was somehow balanced by the eternal coward. The hero with a thousand retreating backs, perhaps. Many cultures had a legend of an undying hero who would one day rise again, so perhaps the balance of nature called for one who wouldn't.

Whatever the ultimate truth of the matter, the fact now was that Death did not have the slightest idea of when Rincewind was going to die. This was very vexing to a creature who prided himself on his punctuality.

Death glided across the velvet emptiness of his study until he reached the model of the Discworld, if indeed it was a model.

Eyeless sockets looked down.

SHOW, he said.

The precious metals and stones faded. Death saw ocean currents, deserts, forests, drifting cloudscapes like albino buffalo herds . . .

SHOW.

The eye of observation curved and dived into the living map, and a reddish splash grew in an expanse of turbulent sea. Ancient mountain ranges slipped past, deserts of rock and sand glided away.

SHOW.

Death watched the sleeping figure of Rincewind. Occasionally its legs would jerk.

HMM.

Death felt something crawling up the back of his robe, pause for a minute on his shoulder, and leap. A small rodent skeleton in a black robe landed in the middle of the image and started flailing madly at it with his tiny scythe, squeaking excitedly.

Death picked up the Death of Rats by his cowl and held him up for inspection.

NO, WE DON'T DO IT THAT WAY.

The Death of Rats struggled madly. SQUEAK?

BECAUSE IT'S AGAINST THE RULES, said Death. NATURE MUST TAKE ITS COURSE.

He glanced down at the image again as if a thought had

struck him, and lowered the Death of Rats to the floor. Then he went to the wall and pulled a cord. Far away, a bell tolled.

After a while an elderly man entered, carrying a tray.

'Sorry about that, master. I was cleaning the bath.'

I BEG YOUR PARDON, ALBERT?

'I mean, that's why I was late with your tea, sir,' said Albert.

THAT IS OF NO CONSEQUENCE. TELL ME, WHAT DO YOU KNOW OF THIS PLACE?

Death's finger tapped the red continent. His manservant looked closely.

'Oh, *there*,' he said. ' "Terror Incognita" we called it when I was alive, master. Never went there myself. It's the currents, you know. Many a poor sailorman has washed up on them fatal shores rather than get carried right over the Rim, and regretted it, I expect. Dry as a statue's ti— Very dry, master, or so they say. And hotter'n a demon's joc— Very hot, too. But you must've been there yourself.'

OH, YES. BUT YOU KNOW HOW IT IS WHEN YOU'RE THERE ON BUSINESS AND THERE'S HARDLY ANY TIME TO SEE THE COUNTRY . . .

Death pointed to the great spiral of clouds that turned slowly around the continent, like jackals warily circling a dying lion which looked done for but which might yet be capable of one last bite.

VERY STRANGE, he said. A PERMANENT ANTI-CYCLONE. AND INSIDE, A HUGE, CALM LAND, THAT NEVER SEES A STORM. AND NEVER HAS A DROP OF RAIN.

'Good place for a holiday, then.'

COME WITH ME.

The two of them, trailed by the Death of Rats, walked into Death's huge library. There were clouds here, up near the ceiling.

Death held out a hand. I WANT, he said, A BOOK ABOUT THE DANGEROUS CREATURES OF FOURECKS—

Albert looked up and dived for cover, receiving only mild

bruising because he had the foresight to curl into a ball.

After a while Death, his voice a little muffled, said: ALBERT, I WOULD BE SO GRATEFUL IF YOU COULD GIVE ME A HAND HERE.

Albert scrambled up and pulled at some of the huge volumes, finally dislodging enough of them to allow his master to clamber free.

HMM . . . Death picked up a book at random and read the cover.

DANGEROUS MAMMALS, REPTILES, AMPHIBIANS, BIRDS, FISH, JELLYFISH, INSECTS, SPIDERS, CRUSTACEANS, GRASSES, TREES, MOSSES, AND LICHENS OF TERROR INCOGNITA, he read. His gaze moved down the spine. VOLUME 29C, he added. OH. PART THREE, I SEE.

He glanced up at the listening shelves. POSSIBLY IT WOULD BE SIMPLER IF I ASKED FOR A LIST OF THE HARMLESS CREATURES OF THE AFORESAID CONTINENT?

They waited.

IT WOULD APPEAR THAT—

'No, wait, master. Here it comes.'

Albert pointed to something white zigzagging lazily through the air. Finally Death reached up and caught the single sheet of paper.

He read it carefully and then turned it over briefly just in case anything was written on the other side.

'May I?' said Albert. Death handed him the paper.

' "Some of the sheep," ' Albert read aloud. 'Oh, well. Maybe a week at the seaside'd be better, then.'

WHAT AN INTRIGUING PLACE, said Death. SADDLE UP THE HORSE, ALBERT. I FEEL SURE I'M GOING TO BE NEEDED.

SQUEAK, said the Death of Rats.

PARDON?

'He said, "No worries," master,' said Albert.

I CAN'T IMAGINE WHY.

The Last Continent by Terry Pratchett will be published in Corgi paperback.

from Ladies' Man

by John Ramster

Ladies' Man is John Ramster's first novel. Aged thirty-one, John Ramster is an opera director who has just completed a tour with Così Fan Tutte *for Glyndebourne. The novel opens with Simon, a laid-back, mellow thirty-something travel agent, whose life is about to change – radically.*

It is a fact that I never had a profound post-coital conversation with anyone until I went straight.

The look on a close friend's face, as I confided in him that I never *really* talked with any of the men with whom I went to bed, remains one of the low points of my life. Astonishment, pity and a trace of contempt all mixed up. I was younger then and subsequently discussed literature, politics and high art with the occasional bemused bedfellow but that total concept of 'let's get completely naked, make love like sewing machines then confide in each other and tell innermost feelings until dawn' continued to elude me.

Until I found myself doing just that. With a woman. And the world changed.

Americans call it a curveball, a baseball term. I just call it fucking *weird* that life can suddenly make something like that happen. Much more odd than the experience of watching a baseball game. Have you ever *seen* a baseball game? The difference between Europe and the USA in one completely pointless non-sport. It is marginally less odd than changing one's sexual orientation but not by much. What happens is that a man runs what is fundamentally a big circle and if he manages to end up back where he started he waves his arms in something approaching relief and celebration. Baseball is strange as well.

Until that point, I never expected to reach the end of my twenties and be in a stable relationship. I knew it could never happen because the job description for being my lifelong companion was far too detailed and specific.

I spent those prime real-estate years of my mid-twenties waiting, wishing and hoping for a best friend to fall in love with me. Soulmates who then become even closer, that was what I thought I wanted. In my wilder, more utopian moments two or even three of my closest friends would declare their passion simultaneously and we would all live together in a big house. I could go around saying, 'Hello, I'm Simon Lyndon; pleased to meet you. Do you know all my husbands?'

I loved my friends so much I was *in* love with them, had fantasies about them, wanted them to be in love with me. But since life isn't like that, this completely shafted any chance of a significant relationship for longer than I dare think about.

And I *did* have my chances, I coulda bin a contendah, he said with a defiant tilt of his chin – I'm not completely unpresentable. I *know* I have great eyes, which are my mother's finest contribution to the Lyndon gene pool, and I always wear a lot of blue to bring them out. I *know* my chest hair is a great 'T' shape (my dad was the same) and I *know* that in a certain light if you squint and look at me full on (slight bump on the bridge of my nose so steer clear of either profile), I'm boyishly handsome and look younger than my thirty, count 'em, thirty years. I'm not thinning on top, thank God. I have exactly seventeen grey hairs on either chestnut temple, not that I have counted. I dress pretty well, more smart than casual, and am adept at covering my Achilles' big butt (my dad was the same).

I've always made the most of what I've got (that cheap trick with the loaves and fishes has *nothing* on me) but I might as well have covered myself in ash and hibernated through my twenties because I never wanted the men who wanted me.

Because, to be more specific, I only ever wanted my straight friends. The ones I couldn't have. The ones who outnumbered the possibly available gay ones two to one. And the awful thing is, I knew this even as it was happening. 'I am an emotional cripple and I am at my peak, fuck it,' I used to think to myself. Then my peak came and went and I tried *not* to think about it.

I have no idea if any of this is normal.

Evidence that it might be vaguely usual for people to have this type of futile sexual fantasy is that many of my straight male friends have taken me to one side and have gruffly told me, '*If I was gay . . .*' and then they talk very fast, '*. . . and-I'm-not-but-if-I-was, I want you to know that you would be the one for me.*'

They are invariably intoxicated when they do this. They look at you like they've just given you a Mercedes for your birthday, they smile at you like Daddy Walton used to smile at John Boy. You want to hurt them so bad you can taste it. They tell you in so many words that a miss is as good as a mile and expect you to admire them for their honesty. Men can be such bastards.

Ladies' Man *by John Ramster will be published by Little, Brown.*

from Chasing the Mountain of Light: Across India on the Trail of the Koh-i-Noor Diamond

by Kevin Rushby

Travel-writer Kevin Rushby journeyed across India tracing the history of the diamond trade. On a cold evening in Old Delhi, after a chance encounter with a shady gem-dealer, he is walking back to his hotel.

The Robbery

A rickshaw pulled up alongside me, the driver peering out from his cab. In the back there were already two men with suitcases, but that was nothing unusual: Delhiites often share transport when necessary. These two were wrapped in Kashmiri shawls and looked frozen.

'Where you going?' asked the driver.

'Karol Bagh.'

The man nearest to me nodded. 'We are going there – our hotel is there.' He had a likeable face: thin with a neat beard. The other was chubby, smooth-shaven, and smiling. 'We can share the cost of our journeying.'

I had heard that one before and it rarely resulted in any savings, but I climbed in. The driver yanked at a cable and managed to slam the engine into gear. We set off.

'Where have you come from?' I asked.

'We are from Himachal Pradesh,' said the chubby one. 'But we come from Bombay – our brother is there.'

The elder one next to me manoeuvred the suitcase on

to his knee and opened it. I caught a glimpse of some clothes. He took out a packet of beedis and offered me one. I refused. He shook the packet. 'It is our custom.'

Reluctantly, I accepted, but no sooner had we got them lit than the rickshaw broke down. The driver got out, muttering to himself. We had only covered about four hundred yards and I was ready to ditch the machine for another, but my fellow-passengers wouldn't hear of it.

'Always hurry – you Westerners,' laughed the older man. 'Hurry, worry, curry. In India you must slow down. Relax.'

I shrugged. It felt wrong to leave while I was still smoking their beedi. Besides, it was a shrewdly persuasive comment – appealing to that side of any traveller who likes to think he has settled into the local pace of things.

The driver spent some time fiddling with pliers then took to smacking at the handlebar with a monkey wrench. There was no anger in what he was doing, no frustration. In all India, with all the broken-down machines I had encountered, I had never seen anyone get angry with any of them. He was simply whacking it as he would whack a lazy donkey. And the rickshaw obviously understood and appreciated his attitude because it started first time when he tried. Patience, I told myself. We set off again.

Our conversation, as I remember it, was fairly innocuous. Places in India. Family.

The rickshaw broke down again. This time in a dark section of road where the sparse traffic sped past oblivious to pedestrians. There were fires burning on the ground and several bundles of rags next to them: sleeping street people, lying like corpses stretched out after a massacre. Here and there a foot or hand stuck out, the flesh black and crusty. We warmed ourselves for a few minutes. None of them moved.

The driver was attempting to rig the gear cable to the windscreen where he could then yank it to change gear. It didn't look hopeful. I went over and thrust ten rupees towards him. 'Here, I'm going to get another rickshaw – take this.'

He waved it away. 'No, no. One minute only!'

The others climbed back inside. 'Come on – he is finished. Come on.'

I dithered. There was no sign of a rickshaw approaching – the usual sickly yellow headlamp wobbling through the darkness. In either direction was a long walk.

'Now he is ready – come on!'

I took my seat. The elder man grinned. 'I think India will teach you many things – like our hospitality, yes?'

He opened the suitcase and took out a packet of biscuits – the ginger snaps you can buy on railway stations. He opened it and offered me one.

'No thanks.'

He shook the packet. 'Come. It is our custom.'

'I really don't want one.'

'Is our Indian food not good enough? We are not rich men, but we offer you freely, as friends.'

It was the bind of courtesy, a silken trap stronger than steel. I took the biscuit.

The engine gunned to life and the driver, grinning happily, helped himself to a ginger snap. I bit off half and ate.

As we jerked into movement, I remember thinking, there is a soft bit here under my fingertip which doesn't seem right, but the first morsel was already sliding down my throat. There was no warning. Perhaps a momentary shutdown in peripheral vision. A twist of darkness. I saw the older man's face smiling at me from the side, looking vaguely like Haile Selassie. Hurry, worry, curry. My head suddenly fell back and hit the metal support of the hood. Then I was unconscious.

At some point during that long night, I woke. I was lying on my back on a concrete floor gazing at the ceiling. I have no idea how long I stared, trying to make sense of a fluorescent tube. My shirt was off and I was covered in dirt and blood, but I had no knowledge of that at the time. All I wanted was to understand that line of light, how the sun could be so stretched and cold.

Later, I had turned my head to the right and could see a group of men squatting on the floor a few feet away from me. Their faces were laughing and hands busy, searching through my bag for the diamonds. Behind was a window covered in shutters – light blue slats, darkness between them. I could not move but did not feel any pain.

One of the men turned and looked at me, said something. They all looked. Chubby and Haile Selassie were both there, with heavy coats across their shoulders against the cold and me half-naked but not cold at all.

I was struggling to get up, at least mentally I was struggling because there was no reaction at all from my limbs. It was as though that gigantic line of light was lying across my chest, pinning me to the ground. Then a shadow came in from above my head and blotted out the light and I saw, as though it were happening to someone else, a syringe come to my arm and the needle slipping inside me. I saw the hands squeeze the plunger and the liquid going in, and I saw the size of that grizzled head close to mine, the greying flourish of a moustache, and in the ear, a lotus flower of eight rubies with a diamond in the centre.

Chasing the Mountain of Light: Across India on the Trail of the Koh-i-Noor Diamond *by Kevin Rushby will be published by Constable.*

from Park and Ride: Travels in a Suburban Land

by Miranda Sawyer
Extract from a work in progress

Forget the Britain that is green and pleasant, urban and dangerous, historical and scenic; Park and Ride *covers the rest of it, the swathes of inbetweeny land, the multiplexed, motorwayed, mind-your-manners Great British Experience.*

You see, Wilmslow used to be a pink jumper, white stilettos kind of a town. Wilmslow girls always wore white stilettos: at school, at party, at pub, at it on the bench outside Barclays Bank. In fact, aside from the pink jumper (slung and knotted around the shoulders), Wilmslow girls wore white everything. White shoes, white miniskirt, white plastic earrings, white streaks in mousy hair, white Consulate cigarettes, white convertible Golf GTi with matching white spoilers. You could spot the odd tinge of colour – turquoise mascara, luminous nail varnish, Marbella-orange legs topped up with brick-red fake tan – but the overall effect was of a poodle that had been put in the washer with Tippex as well as Persil. And then subjected to an eye-wateringly vigorous fur-tonging afterwards.

Wilmslow girls could tong for Britain. They wielded their hair-tongs like light sabres. You know that coffee advert where the attractive young thing tearfully plugs her portable hair-tongs into the cigarette-lighter and then doesn't toast her locks, but heats up her Nescafé instead? That was the kind of thing that Wilmslow girls could never understand. Coffee before curling? Sustenance before scrunch-drying? Really. No wonder the girl was crying. She'd be weeping in shame. In Wilmslow, a half-hour's hard tonging, plus full slap and appropriately co-ordinated jumpsuit were required just to put out the bins. On Saturday afternoons, when Wilmslow girls tripped gigglingly along Grove Street, tinkling their car keys, tossing their root perms, swinging their Ravel bags, it was as if an army of Barbies had come to life, eaten cream buns for a week, and then decided to invade Cheshire. Armed only with hair-tongs and bright white stilettos.

White, white, white. White was so dominant a ward-robe staple, such a uniform of desirable femininity, that my friend Tracey and I joined the tennis club when we were thirteen simply because it was a good opportunity to wear white a lot. We swanned about with our rackets on our shoulders, bobble socks a-bobbling, wristbands a-fluff, poised for a game. But we never got on that well, because we hadn't yet worked out what a tennis club was for.

We'd thought it was a place for playing tennis and working up to all-day snow-hued casualwear. It wasn't. It was a place for picking up tennis players. That was why all the men – burly and blokish, even in their wussy pink tanktops – made all that noise, thumping each other in the biceps, trumpeting scores, snorting like hay-fevered rhinoceri at the punchline to some joke you would never understand. We were too young for them to bother with, but we could see the change when a lady was present. Then, the roaring, fwoarring boys with the flamboyant hip thrusts froze into grinning statues who jingled the change in their shorts pockets.

The lady tennis enthusiasts, though less demonstrative (just a quick nip to the loo for re-tong and lip gloss whenever a man hove into view), certainly weren't any quieter. They never, ever stopped talking, pealing and chiming over one another like a Roy Ayres vibes solo. Despite this, they seemed . . . not prim, but contained, feminine, neat, tucked in, braceleted, cross-ankled, without a fleck of dirt on them. (I still don't know how they managed this. The tennis courts were covered in red sand, which I couldn't help kicking up when I walked on them. I played in a dust cloud, like Pigpen in *Peanuts*. My pristine ensemble kept streaking pink with sweat; vanilla charm ruined by splurges of raspberry ripple. Clearly, my world was not yet up to wearable whites.)

The thing that Tracey and I had failed to understand was that white was the preferred colour for a Wilmslow girl's wardrobe because, despite her seeming independence, her flighty car, her fluffy chatter, her feather earrings, every Wilmslow girl was practising for her wedding day. The Wilmslow World was stuffed with pictures of unblushing brides in swathes of satin-feel polyester. Each looked like a living marquee. And judging by the fierce smile, each was proud to do so. The groom's mood was more difficult to read. Still, if you searched a photo carefully you could usually spot the lucky man, a tiny speck in the background suffocating under several miles of snowy petticoat.

Of course, the joke was that white wouldn't be right once you'd got to your wedding day, haha. At least not if those wild Wilmslow boys had anything to do with it. And as I got older and could read those one-thought expressions beneath those fearsome flicker fringes, the intention in the Action Man grip of those soap-smooth hands, I understood that the wild Wilmslow boys were not the marrying kind. Well, not until they were in their twenties, anyway. Wild Wilmslow boys had wild jobs in 'business', which usually meant they spent their days photocopying or doing deliveries for their dad's firm. They had wild names: John, Mike, Darren. And they had a wild song which they sang on wild occasions, like on the way to the Swan or the King's Arms every single Friday night. It went: Doctor Marten's, yellow laces/Levi jeans with clip-on braces/We're the ones who'll smash your faces/We're the Wilmslow boot boys.

Which was strange because every Wilmslow boy I knew wore a pink jumper. And pulled that chase-me pink jumper over the tidgiest hint of a Boddingtons belly to tuck smoothly into the waistband of pale blue stonewash jeans. And probably straight into the waistband of his pale blue stonewash Y-fronts too. True, a Wilmslow boy strutted with the dick-first swagger of a man from the northwest – what is it about that walk? Is every male born within twenty miles of Manchester taught to toddle like that by law or something? – but he never strutted in *braces*. Also, if a Wilmslow boy was going to smash your face in, no way would he do it in Doctor Marten's. No work boots allowed: he'd never get into the pub for a pint afterwards.

Park and Ride: Travels in a Suburban Land *by Miranda Sawyer will be published by Little, Brown.*

from High on a Cliff
by Colin Shindler

Colin Shindler is the author of the bestselling football memoir Manchester United Ruined My Life. *The following is an extract from his first novel, the funny, tender and heartrending story of a single father's relationship with his son – and a new girlfriend.*

This Helen is American and apparently steak and baked potato and salad is what people have for dinner in America – I thought they just ate hamburgers. When we got home I was sent upstairs to do my homework although I wanted to watch *The Simpsons* first. Usually Dad lets me while he is cooking dinner but this time he got all stern and said I had to start my homework because it would be too late after dinner blah blah blah. I think he was showing off in front of the American woman.

And she is American, this woman, American in her looks and in her way of behaving. Not like my mum. Mum was pretty, Mum was beautiful. She was tall and she had long golden hair like a fairy princess and she wore long flowing dresses. This Helen person is only average in height and her hair is dark and curly, whereas I know for a fact that Dad likes women who have long fair hair. He's always going on and on about how beautiful Mum's hair was because he could run his fingers through it. I think it's a weird thing to do, run your fingers through someone else's hair. I mean, the only person I've ever seen do that is the school nurse and she's just looking for head lice. Is that what grown-ups do when they're making out? Like I said, weird.

In the end Dad did the cooking anyway because Helen's mobile kept ringing. She went into the study where Dad works and then she came back in saying she had to get online to talk to Head Office in America and she asked me if I could help because 'kids know so much more about the Internet than we wrinklies'. It made me want to puke right there.

I was starting to explain that Dad had told me I had to start my homework when Dad interrupted me and said he'd show her how to do it. When he came back he gave me this long lecture about how we always have to be polite to guests and he'd taught me all these manners and why didn't I use some of them occasionally – like now, for instance.

This made me mad because a) I hadn't been rude to Helen anyway, I'd only just met her; it takes time to be rude to someone, and b) how come this system of Dad's about being extra polite to guests only works the one way? Whenever we go to other people's houses Dad tells me how it's not only him who wants to be proud of me but Mum would as well. So when we go out I'm very careful to be polite and what Mum and Dad would call 'the perfect guest'. That means I can't do anything except what other people tell me to do. But when people come to our house I've got to be the 'perfect host' as well, which means I can't do anything and the guest can do whatever she pleases. Now is this unfair or what?

Anyway, Dad decided that I could do my homework after dinner and that I now had to set the table with the best crockery. I thought that was stupid too. We don't normally eat with the best plates and it wasn't like Helen was the Queen or the Prime Minister; she was just somebody from work. And she was getting a false impression of how we normally lived and ate. Particularly since there was live football on the telly. It was only a testimonial match for some old Scottish player who had retired before the start of the season but it was Celtic v. Juventus and Juventus have been the best team in Europe now for years and normally we'd sit in the front room with the plate on our knees and watch the game on TV.

Dad always said it was his work; it wasn't that he wanted to watch it, he had to. (That's a joke of course.) So now, when he had the chance to watch Alessandro Del Piero and that Frenchman with lots of Zs in his name who won the World Cup, we were stuck in the dining room eating off the posh dinner plates.

I mentioned the Juventus game was on television and Dad gave me this look that said 'Shut up, don't talk about it' but what he actually said was, 'Oh, I think Helen would much prefer to talk to you rather than watch a meaningless friendly.' Which was not true. She'd like to be upstairs with Dad, I dare say, rolling about on the bed. Well, as far as I was concerned she could, then I could have watched Celtic v. Juventus.

High on a Cliff *by Colin Shindler will be published by Headline.*

from The Cybergypsies

by Indra Sinha

Indra Sinha has been a cyber-wanderer since 1984, a decade before the world wide web. His obsession with the tortured, fantastic, virtual world has resulted in this book – the personal confession of a cybergypsy.

It's 3 a.m. and I'm online to Jesus Slutfucker. JS informs me that he's typing one-handed, knuckling open a beer with the other. Needs a drink, he tells me. Just got home to find his girlfriend throwing her clothes into a case. She said she was sick of being shackled to a sleazeball, his lifestyle was doing unspeakable things to her head, she was leaving. To emphasize the point, on the way out she stuck a knife in his arse. JS is a nurse, so he knows he's barely scratched, but in any case, it's not the knife that hurt.

i 'm b etter off   w i thou t   t he bitch . . .

He's trying to tough it out, but he's upset. I can tell by the way he's typing, characters detonating on my screen in bursts of venom. What the hell, JS says, he'll celebrate her departure with a few more beers and then settle down to a serious night's buttkicking on the net. Well, in Oklahoma City where he's hunched over his keyboard it's just after nine, so he has the night ahead of him. For me night's nearly over. Something – the moon? my imagination? dawn? – is silvering the sky over the Sussex woods to the east. I've been online for six straight hours and am yearning for bed, but JS is getting into his stride and there's something I want to find out:

>*Geno, friends here in Britain are shitting themselves about a virus called Satanbug. Do you know anything about this one?*

A pause while the satellite relay to the States kicks in . . . The wait is longer than usual. He's thinking. Then the screen comes to life and characters flash across.

>*funny thing, bear, you're the second brit in two days who's asked me about satanbug . . . lady logged in here from the uk, asked if i had it . . . strange girl . . . slasha something or another . . . told me she didn't really like american men because they did not know how to cane a girl the way a british gentleman did . . .*

I'm so astonished that I forget to reply.

>*hey, bear, you still alive . . .? she uploaded a photo. I'll find it, hold on . . .*

. . . 3.21 a.m. in the weald of Sussex. Outside my window, a small animal, probably a rabbit, screams as its life is ended by a fox. There are far more lethal creatures abroad, but no one dreams that they exist.

The night, my love, is full of invisible pathways, criss-crossing the globe, bounced off the stratosphere by orbiting comsats. Along them wander an odd gypsy folk, ceaselessly exploring, always on the lookout for new systems, new people, new information. They congregate, these travellers, at the oases and caravanserais of cyberspace: this bulletin board, that multi-user game. Fifty million people connected to the net, yet all over the world you meet these same few. You come across their spoor on systems in South Africa and Argentina. You bump into them at online parties in San Francisco or Stockholm. Faster than the jet set is this net set. Some are hackers, virus writers – you may never know who they really are. Some may be known to you as scientists, housewives, musicians, policemen, yet in other guises you have probably fought them on multi-user games or flirted with them in that haven of deep roleplayers, the Vortex. These people are the cybergypsies, the explorers of cyberspace. They mapped it and made its links. They named the constellations of its night sky. Theirs were the first camps in cyberspace. They share your secret life, and guilt.

3.25 a.m. Here in Britain respectable computer folk have long since climbed the wooden hill. At this hour, the only hotspots are the really dedicated multi-user games and certain offbeat bulletin boards. On Shades, the serial killers will be lurking. The roleplayers at the mysterious Vortex are still playing out their bizarre fantasies. The software pirates are busy, but on the porno boards, lusts will be subsiding as patrons are forced by the approaching work-day to drag themselves away to solitary beds. Then there are the people like me, the addicts, who drift round the globe with the tide of darkness. It's 9.25 p.m. now in Oklahoma City. New York is just coming alive. The party-ing on the WELL, in San Francisco, won't be in full swing for six hours yet. Nothing significant ever happens on the net before midnight. The catch is that midnight is sweeping round the world at speeds up to and including 1,000 mph. Some modem jockeys like to ride the cusp of darkness round the globe. If you're addicted enough, have unlimited funds and access to chemicals, you can make night last forever, because it's always night somewhere on the net.

. . . 3.27 a.m. Geno's back.

>*found it, yeah, it comes back . . . another thing she likes to talk about is how riding crops are really too nasty to use on human beings, unless they really deserve it . . .:)*

>*This is very peculiar, Geno. Really extremely strange.*

>*thought you limeys would be used to this kind of thing . . . ok stand by to receive slasha . . .*

It's too late at night to explain that it's not the sado-masochism that's weird. What is, is that hours earlier, I'd first heard of the Satanbug virus from a British bulletin-board operator called Josh, whose girlfriend is Carmine. And Carmine is a slender blonde whose bedtime reading is Skin Two catalogues, who attends clingfilm and candlewax parties with the keener Vortex players and has a fondness for the lash. Last time I saw Carmine, she was sheathed in a black rubber dress that clung like a condom, sucking vodka through a leather mask that sprouted nails like porcupine quills—

'Bear, what are you doing?'

My heart leaps like Basho's frog. My wife is standing in the doorway in her nightie, shading her eyes against the light.

'Eve!' I say lamely. 'I thought you were asleep.'

'I can't sleep. What are you doing?'

'Just finishing some writing. I'll be up in a minute.'

'It's three thirty, you've got work in the morning.'

'Don't worry about it.'

She's frowning. I can't tell if she's upset.

'You're not writing. What are you really doing?'

Luckily she doesn't come any nearer. The picture of Slasha has just arrived, Geno is back online, busy hammering his keyboard, the letters come skittering across the screen:

>. . . *maybe all brit women like to be beat, i dunno :) american women seem not to like it so much, one redneck up here just got his dick cut off (real big in the news) for beating and raping his wife* . . .

Eve is shivering. I get up, go over and put my arms around her. She doesn't respond. From the corner of my eye I watch Mr Slutfucker's outpourings scattergun across my screen.

'I'll be up in a second,' I tell her. 'Promise.'

Eve says quietly, 'You do this every night.' She removes herself from my arms and is gone.

I wait till I'm sure she's back in bed, then examine the gif. A blowsy, puffy-faced woman stares out of the screen at me. Nothing like Josh's girlfriend. Coincidence, after all.

The Cybergypsies *by Indra Sinha will be published by Scribner.*

from Always

by Michael Marshall Smith

A remarkable novelist and screenwriter, Michael Marshall Smith has just completed a book of short stories, What You Make It, *in which* Always *appears. Most of his writing is marked by a surreal sense of humour and a dislocated, unnerving view of the world.*

Jennifer stood, watching the steady drizzle, underneath the awning in front of the station entrance. She waited for the cab to arrive with something that was not quite impatience: there was no real hurry, though she wanted to be with her father. It was just that the minutes were filled to bursting with an awful weight of unavoidable fact, and if she had to spend them anywhere, she would rather it were not under an awning, waiting for a cab.

The train journey down from Manchester had been worse, far worse. Then she had felt a desperate unhappiness, a wild hatred of the journey and its slowness. She'd wanted to jig herself back and forwards on her seat like a child, to push the train faster down the tracks. The black outside the window had seemed very black, and she'd seen every streak of rain across the window. She'd stared out of it for most of the journey, her face sometimes slack with misery, sometimes rigid with the effort of not crying, of keeping her body from twitching with horror. The harder she stared at the dark hedges in shadow fields, the further she tried to see, the closer the things she saw.

She saw her mother, standing at the door of the house, wrapped in a cardigan and smiling, happy to see her home. She saw the food parcels her mother had prepared for her whenever she visited, bags of staple foods mixed with nuggets of gold, little things that only her mother knew she liked. She saw her decorating the Christmas tree by herself in happy absorption, saw her in her chair by the fire, regal and round, talking nonsense to the utterly contented cat spread-eagled across her lap.

She tried to see, tried to understand, the fact that her mother was dead.

After her father had phoned she'd moved quickly through the house, throwing things in a bag, locking up, driving with heavy care to the station. Then there had been things to do. Now there was nothing. Now was the beginning of a time when there was nothing to do, no way to escape, no means of undoing. In an instant the world had changed, had switched from a home to a cold hard country where there was nothing but rain and minutes that stretched like railway tracks into the darkness.

At Crewe a man got on and sat opposite. He had tried to talk to her: to comfort her or to take advantage of her distress, it didn't matter which. She stared at him for a moment, lit another cigarette and looked back out of the window. She judged all men by her father. If she could imagine them getting on with him, they were all right. If not, they didn't exist.

She tried to picture her father, alone in the house. How big it must feel, how hollow, how much like a foreign place, as the last of her mother's breaths dissipated in the air. Would he know which molecules had been inside her, cooling as they mixed? Knowing him, he might. When he'd called, the first thing, the *only* thing she could think was that she had to be near him, and as she waited out the minutes she tried to reach out with her mind, tried to picture him alone in a house where the woman he'd loved

for thirty years had sat down to read a book by the fire
and died of a brain haemorrhage while he made her a cup
of tea.

For as long as she could remember there had been few
family friends. Her parents had been a world on their
own, and had no need for anyone else. So different, and
yet the same person, moving forever in a slow comfortable
symmetry. Her mother had been home, her father the
magic that lit up the windows, her mother had been love,
her father the spell that kept out the cold. She knew now
why, as the years went on, her love for her parents had
begun to stab her with something that was like cold
terror: because some day she would be alone. Some day
she would be taken in the night from the world she knew
and abandoned in a place where there was no one to call
out to.

And now, as she stood waiting for a cab in the town
where she'd grown up, she numbly watched the drizzle as
it fell on the distant shore of a far country on a planet the
other side of the universe. The trees by the station road
called out to her, pressing their twisted familiarity upon
her, but her mind balked, refused to acknowledge them.
This wasn't any world she knew.

In three weeks it would be Christmas, and her mother
was dead.

The cab arrived, and the driver tried to talk to her. She
answered his questions brightly.

At the top of the drive she stood for a long moment, her
throat spasming. Everything was different. All the trees,
all the pots of plants her mother had tended, all the stones
on the drive had moved a millimetre. The tiles had shifted
infinitesimally on the roof, the paint had faded a millionth
of a shade. She had come home, but home wasn't there
any more.

Then the front door opened spreading a patch of
warmth on to the drive, and she fled into the arms of her
father.

For a long time she hung there, cradled in his warmth. He was comfort, an end to suffering. It had been him who had talked her through her first boyfriend's abrupt departure, him who had held her hand after childish nightmares, him who had come to her when as a baby she had cried out in the night. Her mother had been everything for her in this world, but her father was the one who stood between her and worlds outside, in the way of any hurt.

After a while she looked up, and saw the living-room door. It was shut, and it was then that finally she broke down.

Sitting in the kitchen in worn-out misery, she clutched the cup of tea her father had made, too numb to flinch from the pain that stabbed from every corner of her mother's kitchen. On the side was a jar of mincemeat, and a bag of flour. They would not be used. She tried to deflect her gaze, to find something to focus on, but every single thing spoke of her mother: everything was something she wouldn't use again, something she'd liked, something that looked strange and forlorn without her mother holding it. All the objects looked random and meaningless without her mother to provide the context they made sense in, and she knew that if she could look at herself she would look the same. Her mother could never take her hand again, would never see her married or have children. And she would have been such a fantastic grandmother, the kind you only find in children's books.

On the kitchen table were some sheets of wrapping paper, and for a moment that made her smile wanly. It had always been her father who bought the wrapping paper, and in years of looking Jennifer had never been able to find paper that was anywhere near as beautiful. Marbled swirls of browns and golds, of greens and reds, muted bursts of life that had lain curled beneath the Christmas tree like an advert for the whole idea of colour. The paper on the table was as nice as ever, some a warm russet, the rest a pale sea of shifting blue.

Every year, on Christmas morning, as she sat at her customary end of the sofa to begin unwrapping her presents, Jennifer had felt a warm thrill of wonder. She could remember as a young girl looking at the perfect oblongs of her presents and knowing that she was seeing magic at work. For her father would wrap the presents, and there were never any joins. She would hold the presents up, look at them every way she could, and still not find any Sellotape, or edges of paper. However difficult the shape, it was as if the paper had formed itself round it like a second skin.

One evening every Christmas her father would disappear to do his wrapping: she had never seen him do it, and neither, she knew, had Mum. In more recent years Jennifer had found the joins, cleverly tucked and positioned so as almost to disappear, but that hadn't undone the magic. Indeed, in her heart of hearts she believed that her father had done it deliberately, let her see the joins because she was too old now for a world where there could be none.

She could remember once, when she'd been a very little girl, asking her mother how Daddy did it. Her mother had told her that Dad's wrapping was his art, that when the King of the Fairies needed his presents wrapped he sent for her father to do it, and he went far off to a magic land to wrap his presents, and while he was away, he did theirs too. Her mother had said it with a smile in her eyes, to show she was joking, but also with a small frown on her forehead, as if she wasn't sure if she was.

As Jennifer sat staring at the paper, her father came back in. He seemed composed but a little shocked, as if he'd seen the neighbours dancing naked in their garden. He took her hand and they sat for a while, two of them where three should be.

And for a long time they talked, and remembered her.

Already time seemed short, and Jennifer tried to remember everything she could, to mention every little thing, to write them in her mind so that they would still be there in the morning. Her father helped her, mixing in his own memories, as she scrabbled and clutched, desperate to gather all the fallen leaves before the wind blew them away.

Looking up at the clock as she made another cup of tea she saw that it was four o'clock, that it would soon be tomorrow, the day after her mother had died, and suddenly she slumped over, crying with the kettle in her hand. Because the day after that would be the day after that day, the week after the week after, next year the anniversary. It would never end. From now on all time was after time: no undoing, no last moment to snatch. There would be so many days, and so many hours, and no matter how many times the phone rang, it would never be her mother.

Seeing her, her father stood up and came to her. As she laid her head on his shoulder he finished making the tea, and then he tilted her head up to him. He looked at her for a long time, and she knew that he, and nobody else, could see inside her and know what she felt.

'Come on,' he said.

She watched as he walked to the table and picked up some of the wrapping paper.

'I'm going to show you a secret.'

'Will it help?' Jennifer felt like a little child, watching the big man, her father.

'It might.'

They stood for a moment outside the living-room door. He didn't hurry her, but let her ready herself. She knew that she had to see her mother, couldn't just let her fade away behind a closed door. Finally she nodded, and he opened the door.

The room she walked into seemed huge, cavernous.

Once cosy, the heart of the house, now it stretched like a black plain far out into the rain, the corners cold and dark. The dying fire flickered against the shadows, and as she stepped towards it Jennifer felt the room grow around her, bare and empty as the last inaudible echoes of her mother's life died away.

'Oh Mum,' she said, 'oh Mum.'

Sitting in her chair by the fire she could almost have been asleep. She looked old, and tired, but comfortably warm, and it seemed that the chair where she sat was the centre of the world. Jennifer reached out and touched her hand. Kissed by the embers of the fire, it was still warm, could still have reached out and touched her. Her father shut the door, closing the three of them in together, and Jennifer sat down by the fire, looking up at her mother's face. What had been between the lines was gone, but the lines were still there, and she looked at every one.

She looked up to see that her father had spread three sheets of the pink wrapping paper on the big table. He came and crouched down beside her and they held Mum's hand together, and Jennifer's heart ached to imagine what his life would be like without her, without his Queen. Together they kissed her hand, and said goodbye as best they could, but you can't say goodbye when you're never going to see someone again. It isn't possible. That's not what goodbye means.

Her father stood, and with infinite tenderness picked his wife up in his arms. For a moment he cradled her, a groom on his wedding day holding his love at the beginning of their life together. Then slowly he bent, and to Jennifer's astonishment he laid her mother out on the wrapping paper.

'Dad . . .'

'Shh,' he said.

He picked up another couple of sheets of paper and laid them on top of her. His hands made a small folding movement where they joined, and suddenly there was only one long piece of wrapping paper. Jennifer's mouth dropped open like a child's.

'Dad, how . . .?'

'Shh.'

He took the end of the sheet lying under her mother, and folded it over the top. Slowly he worked his way around the table, folding upwards with little movements of his hands. Like two gentle birds they slowly wove round each other, folding and smoothing. Jennifer watched silently, cradling her tea, at last seeing her father do his wrapping, and as he moved round the table the two sheets of paper were knitted together as if it were the way they'd always been.

After about fifteen minutes he paused, and she stepped closer to look. Only her mother's face was visible, peeking out of the top. It could have looked absurd, but it was her mother, and it didn't. The rest of her body was enveloped in a pink paper shroud that seamlessly held her close. Her father bent and kissed his wife briefly on the lips, and she bent too, and kissed her mother's forehead. Then he made another folding movement, brought the last edge of paper over and smoothed, and suddenly there was no gap, no join, just a large irregular paper parcel perfectly wrapped.

Then her father moved and stood halfway down the table. He slid his arm under his wife's back, and gently brought it upwards. The paper creaked softly as he raised her body into a sitting position, and then further, until it was bent double. He made a few more smoothing motions and all Jennifer could do was stare, eyes wide. On the table was still a perfect parcel, but half as long. He slid his hand under again, and folded it in half again, then moved round, and folded it the other way, gentle and unhurried. For ten minutes he folded and smoothed, tucked and folded, and the parcel grew smaller and smaller, until it was two feet square, two feet by one, six inches by nine. Then his concentration deepened still further, and as he folded he seemed to take especial care with the way the paper moved, and out of the irregular shape emerged corners and edges. And still the parcel grew smaller and smaller.

When finally he straightened, there was on the table a tiny oblong, not much bigger than a matchbox, a perfect pink parcel. Jennifer moved closer to watch as he pulled a length of russet ribbon from his pocket, and painted a line first one way round, then the other to meet at the top. As he tied the bow she looked closely at the parcel and knew she'd been right all along, that she'd seen the truth as a child. There were no joins, none at all.

When he had finished, her father held the little shape in his hands and looked at her, his face tired but composed. He reached out and touched her cheek, his fingers as warm as they'd always been, and in their touch was a blessing, a persistence of love. All the time she'd been on this planet they had always been there, her father and mother, someone to do the good things for, and to help the bad things go away.

'I can only give you one present this year,' he said, 'and it's something you've already got. This is only a reminder.'

He held up the parcel to her, and she took it. It felt warm and comforting, all her childhood, all her mother's love in a small oblong box. She felt she knew what she should do, and brought the present in close to her, and pressed it against her heart. As she shed her final tears her father held her close and wished her Happy Christmas, and when she took her hand away, the present was gone from her hand, and beat inside her.

The journey back to Manchester passed in a haze of recollection, and when she was back in her flat she walked slowly around it, touching objects in the slanting haze of early morning light. She wished she could be with her father, but knew he was right to tell her to go back. As she sat in the hallway she listened to the beating of her heart, and as she looked at reminders of Mum she let herself feel glad. It would take time, but it was something she already had: she had her mother deep inside her, what she'd been, the love she'd given and felt. She was her mother's pride and joy, and while she still lived her mother lived too: her finest and favourite work, the living sum of her love and happiness. There would be no goodbyes, because she could never really lose her. She could never speak to her again in words, but she would always hear her voice. She would always be inside her, helping her face the world, helping her to be herself.

And Jennifer thought about her father, and knew her heart would soon be fuller still. She knew it would not be many days before another parcel was delivered to her door, and that it too would be perfectly wrapped, its paper a pale sea of shifting blue.

The anthology What You Make It *by Michael Marshall Smith will be published by HarperCollins.*

from Soft

by Rupert Thomson

Rupert Thomson is the author of four highly acclaimed novels, Dreams of Leaving, The Five Gates of Hell, Air and Fire *and* The Insult, *and has been praised by* The Times *as 'a linguistic acrobat'.*

There was nobody to see him off, of course, why would there be? As he waited outside the coach station, a large drop of rain landed on his forehead. It rounded the ridge of scar tissue on the bridge of his nose and rolled into the corner of his left eye where it collected for a moment, like a tear, before spilling down his cheek. Savagely, he reached up, brushed it away. He would never have thought of taking a bus to London, but Sandy Briggs, who worked in the local betting shop, had told him it was cheaper than a train, almost half the price, so here he was, standing on the sloping concrete with his bags. It all felt wrong, somehow. Just looking at the name on the side of the bus gave him an unsteady feeling. Suddenly he wanted to hit someone. Either that, or go to sleep.

Inside, things got worse. There was a toilet in the back that smelled of disinfectant. There were TVs screwed into the roof. A girl slouched in the aisle with a tray of Cornish pasties and cold drinks. She wore a kind of air hostess's uniform and plain black shoes with heels that needed mending. Pinned to her head was a stripy paper hat. You could have turned it upside down and floated it across a pond. *Video Rapide*. He looked out of the window. Tourists in pale pinks and pale greens. Children screaming. The rain still falling, running into big square drains. It was warm, though. Sticky. He shifted inside his clothes, wishing he had worn less.

The bus gathered speed. To the north the sky seemed to be clearing, a thin washed light streaming down into the fields. It wasn't long before the red-brick buildings were gone, the grey rooftops were gone, and they were on the motorway, with nothing to look at, nothing to see, nothing to remind you of anything. Motorways were so empty, the land on either side withdrawn and featureless. If you spent your whole life on a motorway, he thought, you wouldn't remember a thing.

Soft *by Rupert Thomson was published by Bloomsbury.*

from The Adventures of Tom Bombadil

by J.R.R. Tolkien

J.R.R. Tolkien (1892-1973) is best known as the author of the twentieth-century classics The Hobbit, The Lord of the Rings *and* The Silmarillion. *This poem comes from his book of songs, ballads and riddles,* The Adventures of Tom Bombadil.

Shadow-Bride

There was a man who dwelt alone,
   as day and night went past
he sat as still as carven stone,
   and yet no shadow cast.
The white owls perched upon his head
   beneath the winter moon;
they wiped their beaks and thought him dead
   under the stars of June.

There came a lady clad in grey
   in the twilight shining:
one moment she would stand and stay,
   her hair with flowers entwining.
He woke, as had he sprung of stone,
   and broke the spell that bound him;
he clasped her fast, both flesh and bone,
   and wrapped her shadow round him.

There never more she walks her ways
   by sun or moon or star;
she dwells below where neither days
   nor any nights there are.
But once a year when caverns yawn
   and hidden things awake,
they dance together then till dawn
   and a single shadow make.

The works of J.R.R. Tolkien are available
from HarperCollins.

from Fortysomething

by Nigel Williams

Nigel Williams is the author of the bestselling The
Wimbledon Poisoner, *which was also made into a very
successful TV series. A decade or two beyond Bridget Jones
and Adrian Mole,* Fortysomething *holds a funny, painful mirror up to the male psyche. These are the opening
pages of the book.*

12 January, 5 p.m.

Estelle, Ruairghy, Jakob, Edwin and me all at home.

Feeling depressed. Why is this?

Size of stomach? Loss of hair?

Or is it because I am due to be run over by an
articulated lorry on 15 March?

I have been saying for years that I wanted to move on
from my role in *General Practice*, but I suppose I always
thought that I would have some influence over the timing
and manner of my departure. I don't know why I thought
this but I did.

My paranoia is made even worse by the fact that I am
not quite sure who is behind the decision to end Dr
Esmond Pennebaker's life. The new generation of script-
writers, many of whom seem to be younger than my own
children, are trying to pretend that they are only obeying
orders. The producer – a bald, shifty-looking Welshman

called Karl – has been away at a management training course for about a month. I don't think he was quite so bald before the course. He has spoken to no one since his return. If you try to speak to him he twitches and runs away. I don't know what they did to him. All he would say to Surinder, one of the writers, was 'It was very intensive.' Surinder said she had heard they spent ten days trying to construct a Wendy house out of old cardboard boxes. Dave Witchett says they were all forced to type, make phone calls, etc., wearing only their underwear.

I suspect the idea of offing me may have originated with someone at the very highest level in the BBC. Although I have no evidence, I have become convinced that this person is at the bottom of it, and probably insisted too that my death should not give too many opportunities for bravura acting. Someone at the story conference, the week before last, apparently suggested that I fall out of a window but this was quickly squashed. I think I could have done something with that. As it is, all I will get is probably one quick gasp of alarm followed by a muffled scream. It may be – although I can't believe they would do this to me – Death By Reported Speech. A way to go that compounds the tragedy of one's death by handing a dramatic opportunity to another actor. There may be a funeral scene. They may let other actors make speeches. Some of them may even be allowed to cry – something I have never been allowed to do, unless you count the slight tremor at my end of the phone call in which I learned I was being sued by some idiot simply because I had cut off the wrong one of his legs.

Maybe they will let Ronnie 'Very Nice Man' Pilfrey make a speech over the grave. Sicko!

The one clue I have to the identity of those who are trying to kill me is that the decision originated in a committee called the Core Directorate Policy Unit. No one will tell me who is on this committee – although 'some creative personnel' are part of it. If I can work out who they are, and get close enough to them to lick their boots, I may have a chance of surviving this year.

But do I want to? Haven't I had enough?

It is time I moved on. Twenty years in a BBC radio serial is too long. But the time has, as I was telling Estelle the other day, simply flown by. It seems only minutes ago that Esmond Pennebaker was graduating from medical school. Now, here he is about to kick the bucket. What has he done with his life? Gone into the surgery. Had an affair with his secretary. And now here he is – dead, or well on the way to it.

What have I done with my life, come to that?

In a few months too I will be fifty. On the day of our wedding anniversary – 24 June. Estelle does not seem very interested in this fact. I broached the subject casually a few weeks ago, hoping that she might suggest a romantic week away. She has not, so far, done so. The nearest she has come to acknowledging this important landmark in my life was to say, last Tuesday, 'I suppose you want a party.' When I said that I didn't want to put anyone to any trouble, she said, 'Don't go on about it. You keep going on about the fact you are fifty. You are not actually fifty yet. You are forty-nine. I am fifty.'

She isn't actually. She is fifty-one. But I did not like to point out this fact. Instead I said, 'I would like to have a few really close friends round me on the actual day.' She looked at me oddly. 'What friends?' she said, in a way that suggested she thought I had none. 'Oh,' I said. 'Nobby. And Good Old Steve . . .' Estelle said that just because you had known someone for thirty years, that did not necessarily make them interesting. When I asked whether this applied to me, she said I was becoming very self-pitying. She has become very hard, of late. I think this may be something to do with the menopause. I did not, of course, say this. A party is probably a very bad idea. I can't think of who else I would want to ask apart from Nobby, Good Old Steve and Peter Mailer. What, anyway, is there to celebrate about reaching the age of fifty?

9.30 p.m.

Dinner with all the family. This is unusual these days. Estelle made lasagne. She did not, as she once did, make the pasta herself. In fact she has shown a worrying lack of interest recently in things like hand-crafted tagliatelle.

When I chewed her dish in a manner I thought just this side of ostentatious and said, two or three times, 'Mmm! Delicious!' she did not react. So I said, 'My, this is tasty!' She glowered at me from under her fringe and said, 'It's simple anyway.' What does this mean?

Jakob, my middle child, is going back to Oxford tomorrow. On his own. It seems only yesterday, although in fact it was last year, that we were running both Jakob and Ruairghy up to my old university in my elderly Volvo. Two sons at Oxford! A fact for which I had to apologize to other competitive parents in the Wimbledon area. Estelle took to saying that they were 'somewhere in the Midlands', which I thought made it sound as if they were in prison. And tomorrow he will leave Ruairghy behind, here with us.

I love my eldest son dearly but I still think we should have given him a name we could both spell.

It will be strange not to be staggering up the stairs of Jakob's college carrying the portable television, the combined CD cassette-player and radio, the Compaq Deskpro computer, the Hewlett Packard Laserjet 4 printer, the portable answering machine, the three electric guitars, the complete works of John Maynard Keynes and the truly staggering number of Megadeth CDs. I had not even heard of them before 1994, let alone been aware that they had a back catalogue about as extensive as Wagner's.

I asked Ruairghy at dinner tonight whether he was

looking forward to doing some real teaching. He is doing a Diploma in Education at the University of South Wimbledon. His answer surprised me. He said, 'I am not going to be a teacher!' I raised my eyebrows slightly but did not ask why, in that case, he was spending nine months boning up on the theory and practice of education.

My God, it's not long since the first time I left Ruairghy at Oxford. After dumping him in his room with his two mobile phones (in case he lost one, which he did in the first week), his eight T-shirts, two anoraks and three pairs of trainers, I walked back across the quadrangle and sobbed helplessly at the thought that now, at last, 'our boy' was standing on his own two feet.

'Standing on his own two feet' is perhaps, even now, not fully accurate. He asked me the other day where Leeds was. It is possible that we have protected him too much.

Dinner was very pleasant, although Edwin, my youngest, insisted on eating a tin of baked beans out of the can instead of the lasagne. He said lasagne 'hurt his throat'. Edwin is sixteen but I do not think that is a sufficient excuse for his behaviour. Told funny joke which involved the use of the word 'semen' – a noun which always goes down well in our house. Not with Estelle, however. She looked at me frostily. She sometimes says I am 'crude'. Am I? Surely not.

11.30 p.m.

Estelle is asleep. Should I ring Nobby? I don't know why I think talking to Nobby might help me sleep. Hearing about his sex life (which is astonishingly busy for a man of his age) is of course nearly always tiring.

Shall I call Peter Mailer? I think not. Ever since he was cured of alcoholism he has acquired another compulsion. He stares deeply into your eyes and even the most trivial conversational opener provokes him into orgies of sincere nodding. I ascribe this to group therapy.

Good Old Steve? Good Old Steve will be out. I will go to bed. I have the feeling this year is not going to be an easy one.

14 January, 9 p.m.

Jakob back in Oxford. Edwin upstairs (I think). Ruairghy in pub with Gordon. Estelle in bed.

Already missing Jakob. He is in many ways a mysterious, secretive child. When he was young he was particularly fond of hide and seek – and even when he is in the house he often gives the impression of being on the point of disappearing into thin air like the Cheshire Cat. But although he does not say much, his remarks nearly always have a gnomic profundity.

He is a tall, thin boy with a shock of black hair. Estelle often refers to him as 'my handsome one' a remark which I find slightly offensive, but there is no doubt that he has a striking profile and a beautiful speaking voice, as well as an IQ of over 150. Admittedly this was at the age of eight and he may well have dropped a few points since then. But it was tested by no less than three experts, one of whom was German. They all disagreed with each other and Estelle and I averaged out the results.

Estelle always says his intelligence is something to do with his birth – a process he achieved in the world-record time of six and a half minutes from first contraction to first appearance. Apparently (I was in the studio) he emerged suavely from the birth canal, finely covered in black hair and giving a small cynical smile – a fact of which Estelle never tires of reminding him, usually for some reason at family meal times.

I admire Jakob. I admire his ability to remember long telephone numbers, his taste in shoes, his ability to speak Spanish convincingly and to understand his degree course (economics, a science that I find not only dismal but incomprehensible).

And yet . . . and yet . . .

When I asked him the other day which way his ambitions were tending, he muttered something about 'making some serious money'. I had to tell him that when his mother and I met, in the summer of 1968, money was the last thing on either of our minds. 'No,' he said. 'All you thought about was drugs.' I don't know where he got hold of this idea.

Fortysomething *by Nigel Williams will be published by Viking.*

Acknowledgements

The editor and publisher gratefully acknowledge the following for permission to reproduce copyright extracts in this book:

Something for Nothing by Jeffrey Archer, copyright © Jeffrey Archer 1999, is published by kind permission of Jeffrey Archer. Jeffrey Archer's novels are published by Harper-Collins*Publishers*; *The Long Firm* by Jake Arnott will be published by Sceptre, an imprint of Hodder & Stoughton, in July 1999, copyright © Jake Arnott 1999. The extract from *The Long Firm* is published by kind permission of Jake Arnott and Sceptre; *E/P* by David Baddiel will be published by Little, Brown & Co in October 1999, copyright © Fierce Tears Ltd 1999. The extract from the work in progress is published by kind permission of David Baddiel and Little, Brown & Co; *Hens Dancing* by Raffaella Barker will be published by Review, an imprint of Headline Book Publishing Ltd, in June 1999, copyright © Raffaella Barker 1999. The extract from *Hens Dancing* is published by kind permission of Raffaella Barker and Review; *Old Smokeytoes* by Louis de Bernières first appeared in *Marie-Claire* magazine in August 1995, copyright © Louis de Bernières 1995, and is published by kind permission of Louis de Bernières. All novels by Louis de Bernières are published by Vintage Press; *The Consolations of Philosophy* by Alain de Botton will

172

be published in spring 2000 by Hamish Hamilton, copyright © Alain de Botton 1999. The extract *Montaigne and His Books* is published by kind permission of Alain de Botton and Hamish Hamilton. Extract taken from *Michel de Montaigne The Complete Essays* translated by M.A. Screech, published by Allen Lane the Penguin Press, 1991 translation copyright © M.A. Screech, 1987, 1991; *The Spiritual Tourist* by Mick Brown was published in paperback by Bloomsbury Publishing plc in February 1999, copyright © Mick Brown 1998. The extract from *The Spiritual Tourist* is published by kind permission of Mick Brown and Bloomsbury Publishing plc; *The Modern Library: The 200 Best Novels in English Since 1950* by Carmen Callil and Colm Tóibín is published by Picador in April 1999, copyright © Carmen Callil and Colm Tóibín 1999. Extract from *The Molloy Trilogy* by Samuel Beckett copyright © Samuel Beckett 1959, 1976, copyright © Samuel Beckett Estate 1994. The extract from *The Modern Library* is published by kind permission of Carmen Callil, Colm Tóibín and Picador; *Slate Street School* and *Belfast Confetti* are taken from *The Ballad of H.M.S. Belfast: A Compendium of Belfast Poems* by Ciaran Carson, published by Picador in May 1999, copyright © Picador in association with The Gallery Press 1998. *Slate Street School* and *Belfast Confetti* are published by kind permission of Ciaran Carson and Picador; *Honey-Dew* by Louise Doughty will be published by Scribner, a division of Simon & Schuster UK, in May 1999, copyright © Louise Doughty 1999. Quotation from *Have His Carcase*, published by Hodder & Stoughton, copyright © the estate of Dorothy L. Sayers, reprinted by kind permission of David Higham Associates. The extract from *Honey-Dew* is published by kind permission of Louise Doughty and Scribner; *Mapping the Edge* by Sarah Dunant will be published by Virago Press in May 1999, copyright © Sarah Dunant 1999. The extract from *Mapping the Edge* is published by kind permission of Sarah Dunant and Virago Press; *The Loop* by Nicholas Evans will be published by

Corgi in June 1999 and was first published by Bantam Press, both divisions of Transworld Publishers Ltd, copyright © Nicholas Evans 1998. The extract from *The Loop* is published by kind permission of Nicholas Evans and Transworld Publishers Ltd; *Ex Libris: Confessions of a Common Reader* by Anne Fadiman was first published in the USA by Farrar, Straus & Giroux, 1998, and will be published in Great Britain by Allen Lane The Penguin Press in May 1999, copyright © Anne Fadiman 1998. The chapter *My Ancestral Castles* is published by kind permission of the author and Allen Lane The Penguin Press; *Sheer Blue Bliss* by Lesley Glaister was published by Bloomsbury Publishing plc in January 1999, copyright © Lesley Glaister 1999. The extract from *Sheer Blue Bliss* is published by kind permission of Lesley Glaister and Bloomsbury Publishing plc; *Fish* by Sophie Grigson and William Black was published by Headline Book Publishing Ltd in 1998, copyright © Sophie Grigson and William Black 1998. The recipe for *Sea Trout in Filo Pastry with Tarragon* is published by kind permission of Sophie Grigson, William Black and Headline Book Publishing Ltd; *Round Ireland with a Fridge – Again* by Tony Hawks, copyright © Tony Hawks 1999, is published by kind permission of Tony Hawks. *Round Ireland with a Fridge* is published by Ebury Press; *The Proposition* is taken from *Mr Wrong* by Elizabeth Jane Howard, published by Pan, a division of Macmillan Publishers Ltd, in 1975, copyright © Elizabeth Jane Howard 1975. *The Proposition* is published by kind permission of Elizabeth Jane Howard and Macmillan Publishers Ltd; *Epiphany* is taken from *Birthday Letters* by Ted Hughes, published by Faber & Faber in January 1998, copyright © Ted Hughes 1998. *Epiphany* is published by kind permission of Faber & Faber; *The Year 1000* by Robert Lacey and Danny Danziger is published by Little, Brown & Co, copyright © Robert Lacey and Danny Danziger 1999. The chapter *The English Spirit* is published by kind permission of Robert Lacey, Danny Danziger and

Little, Brown & Co; *The Drowning People* by Richard Mason will be published by Michael Joseph Ltd in April 1999, copyright © Richard Mason 1999. The extract from *The Drowning People* is published by kind permission of Richard Mason and Michael Joseph Ltd; *Nathaniel's Nutmeg* by Giles Milton was published by Hodder & Stoughton in March 1999, copyright © Giles Milton 1999. The extract from *Nathaniel's Nutmeg* is published by kind permission of Giles Milton and Hodder & Stoughton; *Tulip Fever* by Deborah Moggach will be published by William Heinemann in May 1999, copyright © Deborah Moggach 1999. The extract from *Tulip Fever* is published by kind permission of Deborah Moggach and William Heinemann; *Dancing Naked in the Mind Field* by Kary Mullis was published in paperback by Bloomsbury Publishing plc in March 1999, copyright © Kary Mullis 1998. The extract from *Dancing Naked in the Mind Field* is published by kind permission of Kary Mullis and Bloomsbury Publishing plc; *Soup and Beyond: Soups, Beans and Other Things* by the New Covent Garden Soup Company will be published by Macmillan Publishers Ltd in May 1999, copyright © New Covent Garden Soup Company 1999. The recipe for *Carrot and Cardamom Soup* from *Soup and Beyond* is published by kind permission of the New Covent Garden Soup Company and Macmillan Publishers Ltd; *What Every Kid Wished Their Parents Knew . . . and vice versa!* by Rob Parsons and Lloyd Parsons will be published by Hodder & Stoughton in June 1999, copyright © Rob Parsons and Lloyd Parsons. The extract from *What Every Kid Wished Their Parents Knew . . . and vice versa!* is published by kind permission of Rob Parsons, Lloyd Parsons and Hodder & Stoughton; *The Tulip* by Anna Pavord was published by Bloomsbury Publishing plc in January 1999, copyright © Anna Pavord 1999. The extract from *The Tulip* is published by kind permission of Anna Pavord and Bloomsbury Publishing plc; *The Last Continent* by Terry Pratchett will be published by Corgi in May 1999 and was first published by

Doubleday, both divisions of Transworld Publishers Ltd, copyright © Terry and Lyn Pratchett 1998. Discworld ® is a trademark registered by Terry Pratchett. The extract from *The Last Continent* is published by kind permission of Terry Pratchett and Transworld Publishers Ltd; *Ladies' Man* by John Ramster will be published by Little, Brown & Co in June 1999, copyright © John Ramster 1999. The extract from *Ladies' Man* is published by kind permission of John Ramster and Little, Brown & Co; *Chasing the Mountain of Light: Across India on the Trail of the Koh-i-Noor Diamond* by Kevin Rushby will be published by Constable & Co in May 1999, copyright © Kevin Rushby 1999. The extract from *Chasing the Mountain of Light* is published by kind permission of Kevin Rushby and Constable & Co; *Park and Ride: Travels in a Suburban Land* by Miranda Sawyer will be published by Little, Brown & Co in June 1999, copyright © Miranda Sawyer 1999. The extract from *Park and Ride* is published by kind permission of Miranda Sawyer and Little, Brown & Co; *High on a Cliff* by Colin Shindler will be published by Headline Book Publishing Ltd in August 1999, copyright © Colin Shindler 1999. The extract from *High on a Cliff* is published by kind permission of Colin Shindler and Headline Book Publishing Ltd; *The Cybergypsies* by Indra Sinha will be published by Scribner, a division of Simon & Schuster UK, in May 1999, copyright © Indra Sinha 1999, ® & © Simon & Schuster Inc. The extract from *The Cybergypsies* is published by kind permission of Indra Sinha and Scribner; *Always* by Michael Marshall Smith was first published in *Darklands 2*, edited by Nicholas Royle, published by Egerton Press, copyright © Michael Marshall Smith 1992, and will appear in *What You Make It* published by HarperCollins*Publishers* in May 1999. *Always* is published by kind permission of Michael Marshall Smith and HarperCollins*Publishers*; *Shadow-Bride* by J.R.R. Tolkien is taken from the anthology *The Adventures of Tom Bombadil* published by George Allen & Unwin in 1962, copyright © George Allen & Unwin Ltd

1962. *Shadow-Bride* is published by kind permission of the J.R.R. Tolkien Estate Ltd and HarperCollins*Publishers*; *Soft* by Rupert Thomson was published in paperback by Bloomsbury Publishing plc in January 1999, copyright © Rupert Thomson 1998. The extract from *Soft* is published by kind permission of Rupert Thomson and Bloomsbury Publishing plc; *Fortysomething* by Nigel Williams will be published by Viking in August 1999, copyright © Nigel Williams 1999. The extract from *Fortysomething* is published by kind permission of Nigel Williams and Viking.

Index of Authors